Glencoe

Common Core State Standards Edition

Project Practice Book

Glencoe Literature **extension projects for**

- **Common Core State Standards**
- **College and Career Readiness**
- **21st Century Skills**

BRITISH LITERATURE

Education

Bothell, WA • Chicago, IL • Columbus, OH • New York, NY

glencoe.com

Send all inquiries to:
McGraw-Hill Education
8787 Orion Place
Columbus, OH 43240

ISBN: 978-0-07-661415-8
MHID: 0-07-661415-8

Printed in the United States of America.

2 3 4 5 6 7 8 9 REL 15 14 13 12 11

The McGraw·Hill Companies

Contents

Reading Lessons: Literature

Reading Lessons: Informational Text

Writing Workshops

Vocabulary

Grades 11–12 Common Core State Standards

Reading Lessons: Literature

from Sir Gawain and the Green Knight

Anonymous

Glencoe British Literature, pages 164–183

RL.11–12.10 Before starting the lesson, read the following selection and complete the lesson activities in ***Glencoe Literature: British Literature.***

from *Sir Gawain and the Green Knight* **(pages 164–183)**

In this lesson you will analyze and discuss the verse romance *Sir Gawain and the Green Knight*. You will then create a virtual multimedia exhibit about Gawain and other Knights of the Round Table. Through your participation in the discussion and your work on the project, you will practice the following standards:

RL.11–12.1
RL.11–12.3

Key Ideas and Details

- Cite strong and thorough textual evidence to support analysis of what the text says explicitly as well as inferences drawn from the text, including determining where the text leaves matters uncertain.
- Analyze the impact of how the author chooses to develop and relate elements of a story (how the characters are introduced and developed).

RL.11–12.4

Craft and Structure

- Determine the meaning of words and phrases as they are used in the text, including figurative and connotative meanings.

Group Discussion

Discussing literature within a small group can help you grow as a reader and as a member of a learning community. Together, you and other group members can arrive at a better understanding of a selection, its ideas and craft, and its connection to other works and areas of study.

PLAN

RL.11–12.1
W.11–12.9, a
W.11–12.10
L.11–12.2b

To prepare for discussion, build your content knowledge by writing answers to the questions that follow, using text evidence. You may also write additional questions about the selection that you wish to discuss with your group. Your teacher may review your answers before the discussion, so be sure to use correct grammar, spelling, punctuation, and capitalization.

RL.11–12.3

Complex Characters Like complex people in life, complex characters in literature are often more interesting than ones that are easily understood and often have more to teach us. **Characterization** is the set of strategies an author uses to develop and convey character. These strategies include description by the narrator, dialogue, and, of course, action.

Name________________________ Class______________ Date______________

1. What are some important ways the author portrays the character of Sir Gawain in the early part of the romance? Write your responses in the chart below.

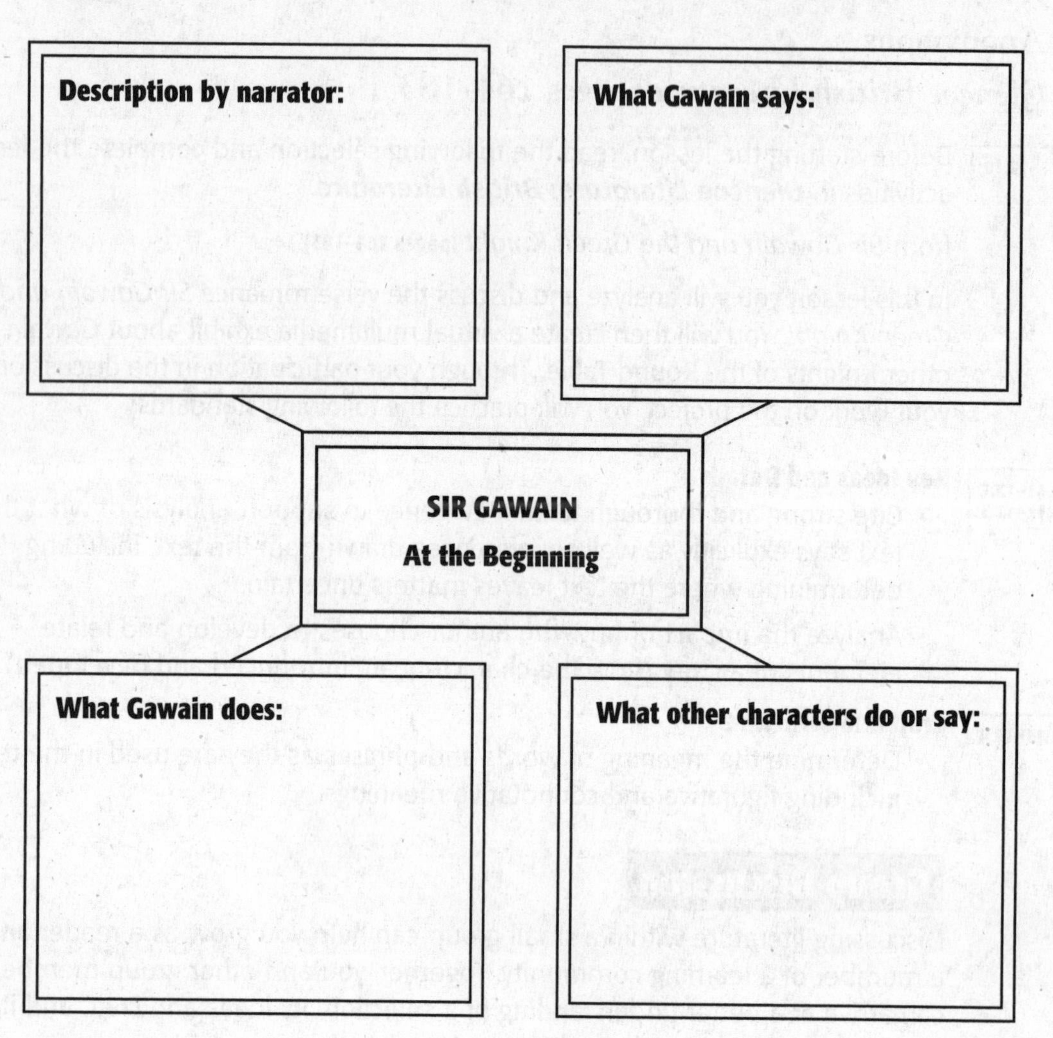

2. Using your responses to the previous question, write a brief character sketch of Sir Gawain as he is portrayed in the early part of the romance.

____

____

____

____

____

Name ______________________ Class __________ Date __________

3. What are some important ways the author has portrayed the character of Sir Gawain by the end of the romance? Write your responses in the chart below.

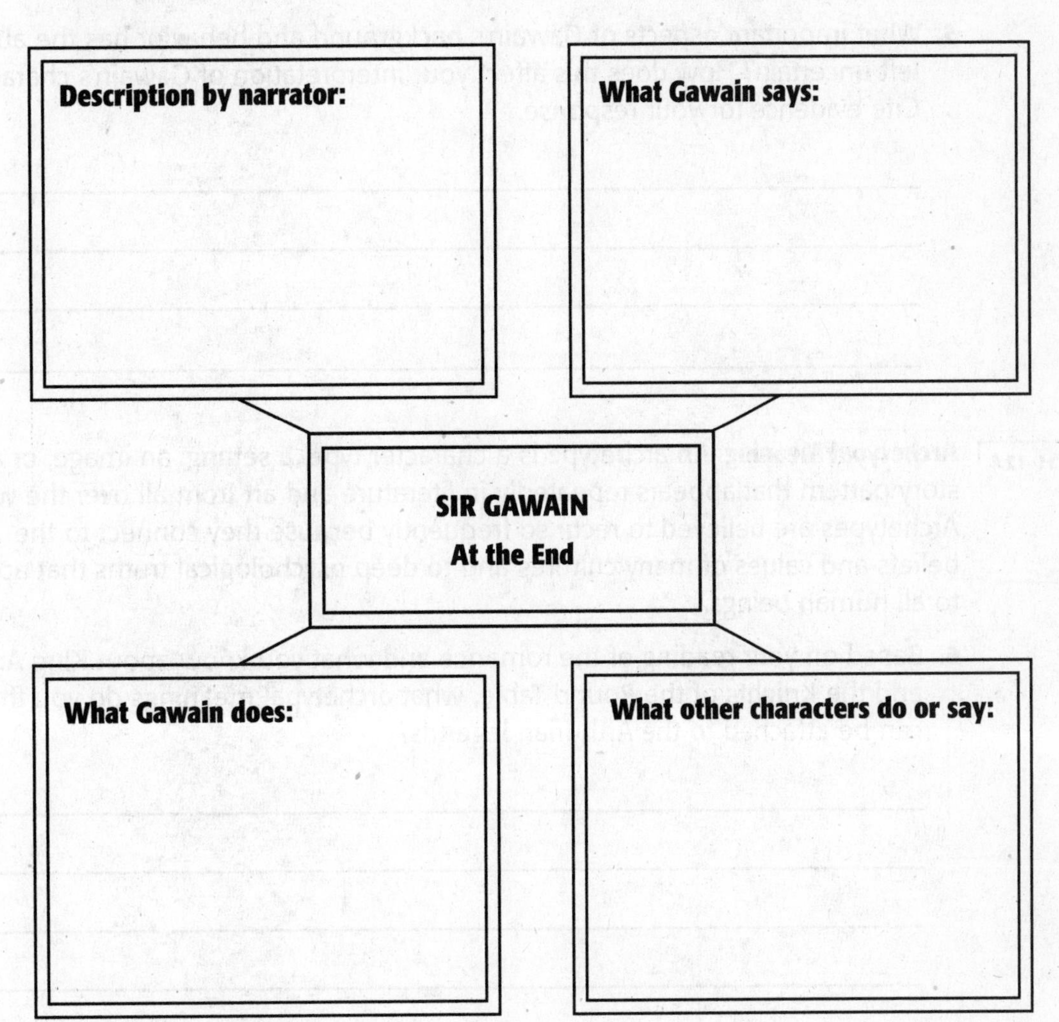

4. Using your responses to question 3, write a brief explanation of how Sir Gawain has changed or become more complex by the end of the romance.

____

____

____

____

Group Discussion

Name ____________________ Class ____________ Date ____________

Group Discussion

RL.11–12.1 **Uncertain Meaning** Some aspects of a text's meaning are often deliberately left uncertain by the author. Determining these uncertainties can be an important part of interpreting the text accurately.

5. What important aspects of Gawain's background and behavior has the author left uncertain? How does this affect your interpretation of Gawain's character? Cite evidence for your response.

RL.11–12.4 **Archetypal Meaning** An archetype is a character type, a setting, an image, or a story pattern that appears repeatedly in literature and art from all over the world. Archetypes are believed to recur so frequently because they connect to the beliefs and values of many cultures and to deep psychological truths that apply to all human beings.

6. Based on your reading of the romance and what you know about King Arthur and the Knights of the Round Table, what archetypal meanings do you think can be attached to the Arthurian legends?

7. What aspects of these archetypal meanings do you think Sir Gawain represents? How do specific words and phrases used to characterize Gawain develop his archetypal meaning in the romance?

Name______________________________ Class______________ Date______________

SL.11–12.1,a,b

ASSIGN

Meet with your literature group to plan your discussion. Each group member should become the expert on one or more of the questions answered on pages 4–6. Each expert will then guide the discussion on his or her question(s). List each group member and the question(s) he or she will become an expert on in the chart below.

Group Member	Question(s) to Present

To become an expert on your question(s), spend some extra time thinking about your question(s) and consulting the text for relevant details. Building on your question(s), write down one or two discussion points or related questions for group members to consider as they explore text issues.

____

____

____

____

____

____

Group Discussion

Name ______________________ Class ____________ Date ____________

Group Discussion

DISCUSS

RL.11–12.1
RL.11–12.3
RL.11–12.4
SL.11–12.1
a, c, d

Break into your assigned literature group to conduct your discussion. The expert for question 1 should begin by reading aloud the question and leading the discussion in response. Follow this process for each question until you have covered them all.

Remember that literature groups contain room for disagreement. Healthy debate can help all members push their understanding to a new level. Use your time wisely so that you are able to discuss all the questions sufficiently.

In your discussion, follow the guidelines below.

Discussion Guidelines
• Come to discussions prepared; be sure you have carefully and thoroughly answered all questions. • Express your ideas clearly. When presenting on your question and commenting on others, support your ideas with concrete evidence from the text. Give specific page numbers. • Work with your group to promote civil, democratic discussions and decision making. • Work with your group to set clear goals and deadlines. • Establish individual roles as needed (i.e., note taker, moderator, etc.). • Propel conversations by posing and responding to questions that probe reasoning and evidence. • Ensure a hearing for a full range of positions on a topic or issue; clarify, verify, or challenge ideas and conclusions; and promote divergent and creative perspectives. • Respond thoughtfully to diverse perspectives and synthesize comments, claims, and evidence made on all sides of an issue. • Resolve contradictions when possible and determine what additional information or research is required to deepen the investigation or complete the task.

At the end of your discussion, be prepared to share the insights you have gained with your class. On the lines below, briefly summarize the most interesting ideas or insights you heard or experienced during the discussion.

____

____

____

____

____

____

Name________________________ Class____________ Date____________

from Sir Gawain and the Green Knight

Anonymous

21st Century Skills Project Virtual Multimedia Exhibit

Now that you have analyzed and discussed the poem excerpt in detail, you will have the opportunity to extend your thinking about it creatively by completing a group project. Your assignment is to develop content for a Web page that presents a virtual multimedia exhibit about the legendary Knights of the Round Table. In carrying out this project, you will follow the steps below:

- Conduct research about King Arthur and the Knights of the Round Table.
- Write, gather, and organize content for a virtual multimedia exhibit.
- If resources allow, build a Web page featuring your exhibit on the Internet.

PART 1 Develop Content for a Virtual Exhibit

With a small group, find source material about the Knights of the Round Table. Using the information you gather, develop content for a virtual multimedia exhibit that profiles the different knights and the legendary events with which they are connected.

W. 11–12.7
W. 11–12.8
W. 11–12.9

Conduct Research Using reliable print and online resources, such as reference works or university Web sites, gather information in a variety of media about the Knights of the Round Table. (See Glencoe Literature pages R31–R37 for information about finding, evaluating, and documenting sources.)

Good sources could include classic and modern versions (written, dramatic, and cinematic) of the King Arthur legends and works of art depicting the knights such as paintings or illustrations. You might also consult mythological or archetypal studies of the legends that connect the knights to specific qualities or meanings. See if you can find tables of statistics related to the different knights, their backgrounds, and their achievements. Take notes as you research and label media files carefully so that you can organize and use them later. Use the questions on the following page to guide you.

Name________________________ Class______________ Date______________

1. Create a list of the Knights of the Round Table that you will include in your exhibit. Be sure to include Arthur and Gawain. You may want to assign each member of the group one or two knights to research. You will find it easier to locate information about the better-known knights.

1. ____________	5. ____________	9. ____________
2. ____________	6. ____________	10. ____________
3. ____________	7. ____________	11. ____________
4. ____________	8. ____________	12. ____________

2. For each of the knights on your list, create a profile sheet like the one below. Make as many copies of this page as you need to complete your work.

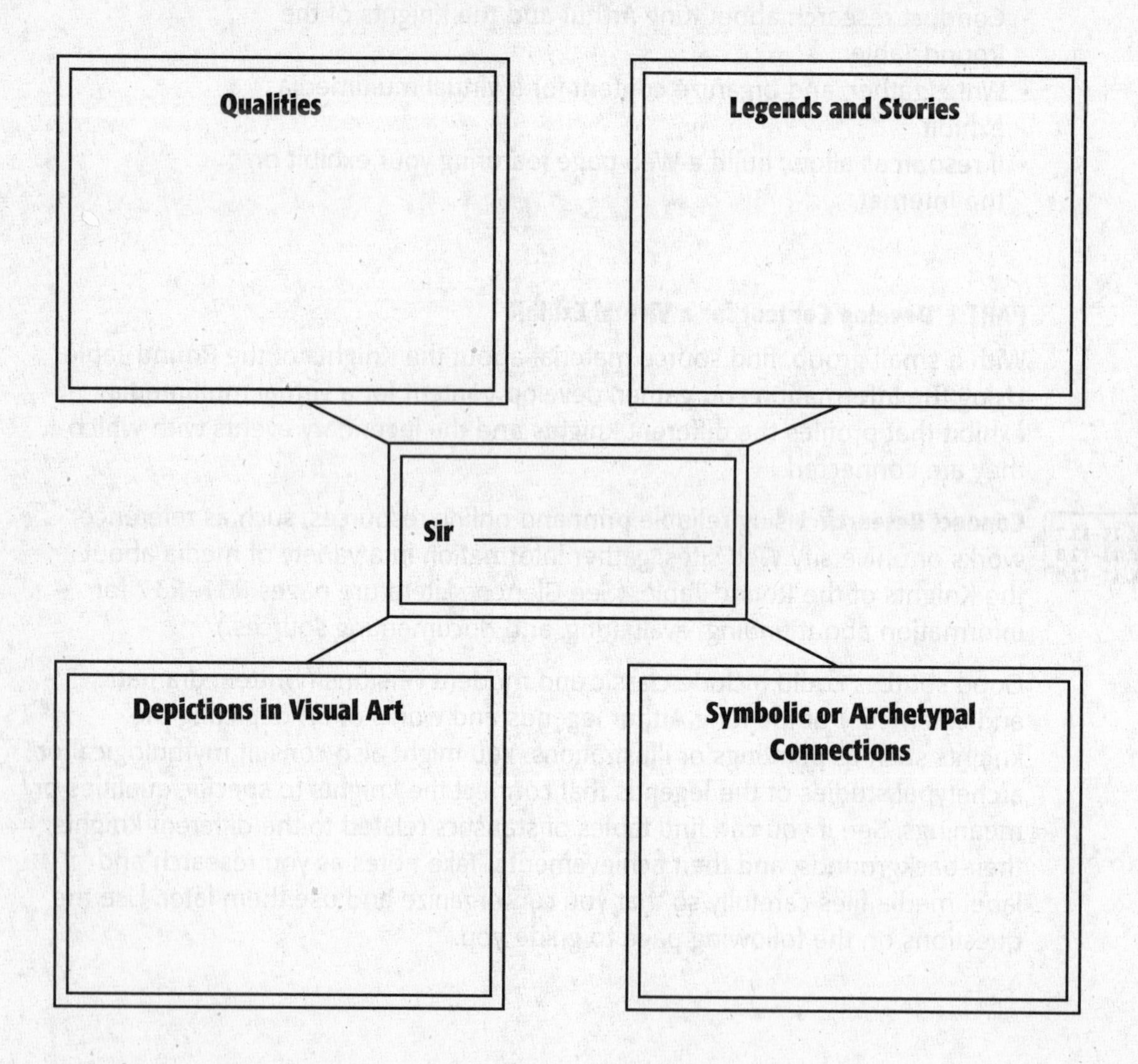

Name______________________ Class__________ Date__________

3. Using the information you have gathered about each knight on his profile sheet, write a brief profile to introduce this knight to visitors to your virtual exhibit. Then complete the planning section at the bottom of the page. Make as many copies of this page as you need to complete your work.

Sir ____________________

____

____

____

____

____

____

W.11–12.8

4. Decide what multimedia files you want to include in your virtual exhibit for this knight. Describe the content of each file and make a note of the file name, type, and location. Keep track of your sources so you can credit them later.

Legend Excerpts	Paintings or Sculptures	Book Illustrations	Manuscript Illuminations	Movie Stills or Footage

21st Century Skills Project

Name________________________ Class______________ Date______________

SL.11–12.5 **Design Your Exhibit** After you've finished conducting and organizing your research, you'll need to decide on the presentation and navigation of your exhibit. For help with this task, answer the questions below.

1. How will you introduce your exhibit? What will its title be? What text, images, and links will appear on the home page?

2. If you have separate links for each knight, what will appear on them? What second-level links will you have on these pages? How will the links be organized or categorized for easier navigation?

3. What types of content will the second-level links take exhibit visitors to? How will you make sure that the purpose and connection of the content is clear?

21st Century Skills Project

Name______________________________ Class______________ Date______________

Create Content Decide which group members will be responsible for designing and writing each page of the exhibit. Look at other Web pages and wikis (a wiki page is part of a collection of interlinked pages with a Web browser) online to get ideas about how to break up the text and engage visitors.

After all the content is written, peer review each other's work and make sure it all flows together logically and supports the main idea you wanted to convey. Follow the citation guidelines on pages R35–R37 of your textbook to credit your sources.

Once you have created all the content for your virtual exhibit, construct a site map that visitors to your virtual exhibit can link to from the home page. Organize your site map like an outline, a decision tree, or whatever works best for the content you present. Sketch your chosen site map structure in the space below.

Name________________________ Class____________ Date____________

Present Your Web Page Content If you are not going on to Part 2 of this 21st Century Skills Project, your teacher may ask you to present your Web page content as the end result of the project. You may also be evaluated on the presentation.

Display your Web page content in a written or typed format that is visually appealing and presents the information clearly. If you have plans to include hyperlinks, indicate where these would appear by underlining the relevant text to be linked and including footnotes that summarize what each link is about. You could also include sample print-outs of the links and number them to match your footnotes. Once your group is satisfied that the content is presented effectively, turn it in to your teacher.

PART 2 Build a Web Page

W.11–12.6

After you've finished Part 1 of this project, build a Web page for your content. If your school or class already has a wiki, you may want to add your content as a wiki page. There are also many sites that will allow you to create your own Web page for free. These types of sites often provide templates and are easy to use. If you want more freedom with your design and navigation and you're familiar with HTML coding and other technical aspects, try to build your page from scratch.

Make sure the information on your page is visually appealing, clearly presented, and easy to navigate. Use headings to introduce topics and break up text. Check to make sure you've included all necessary hyperlinks and that they work.

Name________________________ Class______________ Date______________

After you've completed this project, answer the following questions.

1. How well does your Web page convey information about the Knights of the Round Table?

____

____

____

____

2. Is your Web page easy to navigate? Is information presented clearly? Explain.

____

____

____

____

3. What would you change in the planning, creation, and presentation of this project if you were to do it again?

____

____

____

____

Name______________________ Class__________ Date__________

SL.11–12.1, b, c, d

Evaluate As you read and view your classmates' work, take notes about the content and effectiveness of their Web pages. Then use your notes to participate in a class discussion about the project.

1. Does the concept of this virtual exhibit on Knights of the Round Table make sense? Is it adequately carried out? Explain.

____

____

____

____

2. Is the information in the exhibit presented clearly and effectively? Explain.

____

____

____

____

3. What would you add or change in the exhibit? Why? Consider the content, design, and navigation.

____

____

____

____

21st Century Skills Project

Name ________________ Class ________ Date ________

Group Discussion

The Tragedy of Macbeth

William Shakespeare

Glencoe Literature: British Literature, 306–396

RL.11–12.10 Before starting the lesson, read the following selection and complete the lesson activities in ***Glencoe Literature: British Literature.***

Macbeth **(pages 306–396)**

In this lesson you will compare and evaluate at least two interpretations of Shakespeare's *Macbeth*. You will then write a critical review to introduce your preferred interpretation and to explain what makes it unique and worthwhile. Through your participation in the discussion and your work on the project, you will practice the following standards:

RL.11–12.1 **Key Ideas and Details**

- Cite strong and thorough textual evidence to support analysis of what the text says explicitly as well as inferences drawn from the text.

RL.11–12.7 **Integration of Knowledge and Ideas**

- Analyze multiple interpretations of a story, drama, or poem, evaluating how each version interprets the source text.

After you have studied Shakespeare's source text, you should review at least two interpretations of it by doing one or more of the following. Make sure that you take notes either during or immediately after your review. To preview the kind of information you will need to record, page ahead to the questions that follow.

- View a stage production or productions of *Macbeth* (live or recorded, professional or amateur)
- View a film adaptation of the play
- Read a graphic novel adaptation of the play
- Read a good-quality narrative retelling of the story
- View an opera version of the play (live or recorded)

As you explore possibilities, consider a version of the story set in a different time and place. The Kurosawa film *Throne of Blood*, which is discussed on pages 398–401 of *British Literature*, is an adaptation of the script both for the film medium and for a historical setting in medieval Japan.

Name______________________ Class______________ Date______________

Group Discussion

Group Discussion

Discussing literature within a small group can help you grow as a reader and as a member of a learning community. Together, you and other group members can arrive at a better understanding of a selection, its ideas and craft, and its connection to other works and areas of study.

PLAN

RL.11–12.1
W.11–12.9a
W.11–12.10
L.11–12.1
L.11–12.2b

To prepare for discussion, build your content knowledge by examining the source text and interpretation(s) in greater detail. On your own, write your answers to the questions that follow, as well as any additional questions you think need to be addressed. Your teacher may review your answers before the discussion, so be sure to use complete sentences and correct spelling, punctuation, and capitalization.

RL.11–12.2
RL.11–12.3
RL.11–12.5

Elements of a Tragedy As a dramatic work in the tragic mode, Shakespeare's text has the following major elements:

- **Plot** A tragic plot structure (including exposition, rising action, a climax, and a resolution) that shows a logical sequence of events leading a person of high rank or status to a tragic fall and death
- **Tragic Hero** A main character with a tragic flaw who brings about his or her own downfall
- **Supporting Characters and Foils** Other characters who interact with the tragic hero and/or help bring his qualities and flaws into relief
- **Dialogue and Soliloquies** Conversations and speeches that reveal characters' thoughts and feelings and/or indicate action, mood, or theme
- **Setting and Stage Directions** Instructions for the enactment of the script that indicate setting, character, action, and stage effects
- **Theme** The lesson or meaning implied in the tragic hero's downfall and in other aspects of the play

For each of the interpretations you review, identify the elements of Shakespeare's source text that the interpretation changes or approaches in an individual way. Look closely at how Shakespeare has handled these elements. Then use what you have learned about Shakespeare's approach to analyze that of the interpretation more closely. Write your responses in the charts that follow.

Name________________ Class__________ Date__________

1. Your analysis of Interpretation 1:

Elements of a Tragedy	How Shakespeare handles this element in the source text	How this element is handled in Interpretation 1, [add title] ________
Tragic Plot		
Tragic Hero		
Supporting Characters and Foils		
Dialogue and Soliloquies		
Setting and Stage Directions		
Theme		

Group Discussion

Name______________________________ Class______________ Date______________

2. Your analysis of Interpretation 2:

Elements of a Tragedy	How Shakespeare handles this element in the source text	How this element is handled in Interpretation 2, [add title] ______________
Tragic Plot		
Tragic Hero		
Supporting Characters and Foils		
Dialogue and Soliloquies		
Setting and Stage Directions		
Theme		

RL.11–12.7 **Genre Elements** If either of the interpretations you are analyzing is in a different genre from Shakespeare's *Macbeth*, describe any elements of that genre that are relevant to your analysis. For example, if you are reviewing a film version of the play, include descriptions of elements such as shot composition or sequence editing if they play an important role in the unique impact of the interpretation.

3. Genre elements that contribute to the impact of Interpretation 1:

Genre: ______________ Genre Elements	What resource(s) does this element give the author of Interpretation 1 that Shakespeare did not have?	How does the author of Interpretation 1 use this element to put a unique stamp on Interpretation 1?

Name________________________ Class______________ Date______________

4. Genre elements that contribute to the impact of Interpretation 2:

Genre: ____________ **Genre Elements**	**What resource(s) does this element give the author of Interpretation 2 that Shakespeare did not have?**	**How does the author of Interpretation 2 use this element to put a unique stamp on Interpretation 2?**

Group Discussion

5. Basing your responses on your answers to the preceding questions, summarize how each of the interpretations presents a unique perspective on the source text. Then give your evaluation of the success of the interpretation. Support specific points in your evaluation with evidence from the interpretation.

Interpretation 1 Title: ________________________________

Summary: ________________________________

____

____

Evaluation: ________________________________

____

____

Evidence: ________________________________

____

____

____

Name ______________________ Class ____________ Date ____________

Interpretation 2 Title: ______________________

Summary: ______________________

Evaluation: ______________________

Evidence: ______________________

6. Which of these two works do you think is the better interpretation of Shakespeare's source text? In your response, describe the criteria on which you are basing your judgment and how your preferred interpretation meets those criteria.

Name ____________________ Class ____________ Date ____________

SL.11–12.1, a,b,d

ASSIGN

Meet with your literature group to plan your discussion. Each group member should become the expert on one or more of the questions on pages 18–22. Each expert will then guide the discussion on his or her question(s). List each group member and the question(s) he or she will become an expert on in the chart below.

Group Member(s)	Question(s) to Present

To become an expert on your question(s), spend some extra time thinking about your question(s) and consulting the source text and the interpretations for relevant details. Building on your question(s), write down one or two discussion points or related questions for group members to consider as they explore text issues.

____

____

____

____

____

____

Name______________________ Class__________ Date__________

Group Discussion

DISCUSS

SL.11–12.1 a–d
SL.11–12.2
SL.11–12.4

Break into your assigned literature group to conduct your discussion. The expert for question 1 should begin by reading aloud the question and leading the discussion in response. Follow this process for each question until you have covered them all.

Remember that literature groups contain room for disagreement. Healthy debate can help all members push their understanding to a new level. Use your time wisely so that you are able to discuss all the questions sufficiently.
In your discussion, follow the guidelines below.

Discussion Guidelines
▪ Come to discussions prepared; be sure you have carefully and thoroughly answered all questions. ▪ Express your ideas clearly. When presenting on your question and commenting on others, support your ideas with concrete evidence from the text. Give specific page numbers. ▪ Work with your group to promote civil, democratic discussions and decision making. ▪ Work with your group to set clear goals and deadlines. ▪ Establish individual roles as needed (e.g., note taker, moderator, etc.). ▪ Propel conversations by posing and responding to questions that probe reasoning and evidence. ▪ Ensure a hearing for a full range of positions on a topic or issue; clarify, verify, or challenge ideas and conclusions; and promote divergent and creative perspectives. ▪ Respond thoughtfully to diverse perspectives and synthesize comments, claims, and evidence made on all sides of an issue. ▪ Resolve contradictions when possible and determine what additional information or research is required to deepen the investigation or complete the task.

Name_______________ Class__________ Date__________

The Tragedy of Macbeth

William Shakespeare

21st Century Skills Project Critical Review

Now that you have analyzed and discussed the interpretations of *Macbeth* in detail, you will have the opportunity to extend your thinking about it by completing a project. Your assignment is to write a critical review. As you proceed, refer as necessary to the criteria and steps for writing a critical review in the writing workshop in *Glencoe Literature: British Literature* (pages 1316–1323).

If resources allow, you can publish your review online. If you do, you'll be able to add links to images and other media to help elaborate on the ideas and arguments in your review. Keep this in mind as you write.

PART 1 Write a Critical Review

RL.11–12.1
W.11–12.1
W.11–12.9, a
W.11–12.10

Using the ideas and issues covered in your analysis and discussion of the interpretations, write a critical review of the interpretation you think is more successful. Begin by answering the questions below. You may write directly on these pages or use the space given for notes and compose your draft on a computer. Be sure to ask what your teacher prefers.

1. What makes this version a successful, worthwhile interpretation of Shakespeare's source text? Put your answer into the form of a thesis sentence that states the main idea of your essay. Then think about how you will introduce the thesis, provide a context for your review, and connect with your audience. Use your ideas to compose an introduction to your review.

____

____

____

____

____

____

____

21st Century Skills Project

Name__________________ Class__________ Date__________

2. What are your main supporting ideas for your thesis? What details, sub-ideas, or examples do you need to include to defend these ideas successfully?

Main Idea	Main Idea	Main Idea	Main Idea
Supporting Information:	Supporting Information:	Supporting Information:	Supporting Information:

3. What would be the most logical and effective order in which to present these supporting ideas? What connections and transitions between them will you use? Write your responses in the form of an outline on a separate sheet of paper or on a computer.

Name______________________ Class__________ Date__________

4. What concrete examples from the interpretation will you bring in to support ideas or illustrate points? After you have made your list, go back to your outline and indicate where these materials will be used.

Images from stage productions or movie stills:
Posters or other promotional material for the interpretation:
Video footage:
Facsimiles of book pages:
Drawings or illustrations:
Sound recordings:
Physical objects such as props or costumes:

21st Century Skills Project

Name________________ Class________________ Date________________

5. Using your outline, draft the body of your review on separate sheets of paper or on a computer.

6. What idea do you want to repeat or introduce to sum up your argument? How can you send your reader away strongly motivated to experience the interpretation you have written about? Use your ideas to compose a concluding paragraph for your review.

____

____

____

____

____

____

____

____

Present Your Review If you are not going on to Part 2 of this 21st Century Skills Project, your teacher may ask you to present your review orally as the end result of the project. You may also be evaluated on the presentation.

Before you present your review to the class, practice presenting it orally on your own and in front of family members or friends. Don't rush your delivery. Use your organization and transitions to help you determine when to pause or vary your pace. Speak clearly and look at your audience. Try to memorize some, if not all, of your review so that you don't have to read off your paper throughout your presentation. Vary your intonation to get your meaning across and to emphasize key words or ideas.

Name________________________ Class______________ Date______________

PART 2 Publish Online

SL.11–12.5 After you've finished Part 1 of this project, publish your review online in an interactive format that includes an audio recording of the essay and hyperlinks to images and other visual media (such as video clips). Make strategic use of digital media to enhance understanding of your presentation and critique of the *Macbeth* interpretation.

SL.11–12.6 **Audio Recording** Before you record your review, practice reading it aloud. Don't rush as you read. Use your punctuation and logical transitions to determine where to pause or vary your pace. Be sure to adapt your speech to the context. For example, if your review is written in formal language, don't read it with an informal tone of voice. When you feel prepared, record your review.

Links to Visual Media When you publish your review, you will include hyperlinks to visual or sound media, which will give concrete examples related to the ideas and arguments you've presented. These links will help your readers get a better understanding of the interpretation you reviewed. For example, if you wrote a review about a film version of the play in an unusual setting, you might link your description of that setting to a photo of it. Pay attention to copyright information when you choose your media. Include credit information if you need to. In some cases you may want to link to uploaded images or recordings that you have created yourself.

Before you publish your review, fill in the chart below to help you decide what images and/or other media you want to link to.

Section of Review	Outline Number(s)	Corresponding Media Link

21st Century Skills Project

Name________________________________ Class______________ Date______________

W.11–12.6 **Publish and Present** After you've completed your chart, decide where you will publish your review. If your school already has a Web site for student work, you might consider publishing your review there. You can also search online for Web sites that allow you to create your own page for free. These types of sites often provide templates and are easy to use.

Publish your review on your chosen site. Using your chart as a guide, hyperlink various sections of your review to images, sound recordings, and other media related to the interpretation or your critique of it. Add a hyperlink to your audio recording at the beginning of the review. When you are finished, send the URL of your site to your teacher and classmates so they can read and view your work.

After you've completed this project, answer the following questions.

1. How does your audio recording add to the presentation of your review?

____

____

____

____

2. Which parts of your review led to the most interesting links? Why?

____

____

____

____

3. What would you change in the planning, creation, and presentation of this project if you were to do it again?

____

____

____

____

21st Century Skills Project

Name________________________ Class____________ Date____________

SL.11–12.1, b, c, d

Evaluate Read your classmates' reviews once without clicking on any of the links so that you understand the content. Then read the reviews a second time and click on the links to see the media and hear the audio recording. As you read and view your classmates' work, take notes about the content and effectiveness of their reviews and related media. Use your notes to participate in a class discussion about the project.

1. How well does the review present the interpretation it is about? How effectively does it motivate the reader to experience the interpretation? Explain.

____

____

____

____

2. Does the audio recording add to or detract from your understanding of the review? Explain.

____

____

____

____

3. How well do the links to visual and sound media connect to ideas in the review? Explain.

____

____

____

____

21st Century Skills Project

4. What would you add or change in the review or the accompanying visual media? Why?

____

____

____

____

Name______________________ Class__________ Date__________

Group Discussion

Ode on a Grecian Urn

John Keats

Glencoe British Literature, pages 830–834

RL.11–12.10 Before starting the lesson read the following selection and complete the lesson activities in *Glencoe British, Literature.*

"Ode on a Grecian Urn" **(pages 830-834)**

In this lesson you will analyze and discuss John Keats's poem "Ode on a Grecian Urn." You will then write a poem of your own that you can publish online. Through your participation in the discussion and your work on the project, you will practice the following standards:

RL.11–12.2 **Key Ideas and Details**

- Determine two or more themes or central ideas of a text and analyze their development, including how they interact and build on one another.
- Provide an objective summary of the text.

RL.11–12.4
RL.11–12.5 **Craft and Structure**

- Determine the meaning of words and phrases as they are used in the text, including figurative and connotative meanings.
- Analyze the impact of specific word choices on meaning.
- Analyze how an author's choices concerning how to structure specific parts of a text contribute to its overall structure and meaning as well as its aesthetic impact.

Group Discussion

Discussing literature within a small group can help you grow as a reader and as a member of a learning community. Together, you and other group members can arrive at a better understanding of a selection, its ideas and craft, and its connection to other works and areas of study.

Name______________________ Class__________ Date__________

Group Discussion

PLAN

RL.11–12.1
W. 11–12.9, a
W. 11–12.10
L. 11–12.1
L. 11–12.2, b

To prepare for discussion, build your content knowledge by examining the selection in greater detail. On your own, write your answers to the questions that follow using text evidence. You may also write additional questions about the selection that you wish to discuss with your group. Your teacher may review your answers before the discussion, so be sure to use complete sentences and correct spelling, punctuation, and capitalization.

RL.11–12.2
RL.11–12.5

Structure Keats's ode is divided into five equal sections of ten lines apiece. Each section conveys one or more key ideas that, in the order presented, support the theme of the poem.

1. How would you summarize the key idea(s) in each section of the poem? Write your responses in the following chart.

Section	Summary of Key Ideas
1	
2	
3	
4	
5	

Name ______________________ Class __________ Date __________

2. According to the speaker of the poem, what advantages and disadvantages do the lovers depicted on the urn have to those in the real world? Why does the speaker think their situation is preferable to that of real, living lovers?

____

____

____

____

3. What does it mean to say that "beauty is truth, truth beauty"? Why is this all the wisdom that people on earth need?

____

____

____

____

4. How in your own words would you state the theme of the poem?

____

____

____

____

RL.11–12.4
L.11–12.5, b

Word Choice In section 3 Keats uses the word *happy* six times, indicating that it is an important word and one he chose carefully, even though to modern ears it may sound very general.

5. Use a print or online dictionary to look up the etymology of the word *happy*. Then explore nuances in the word's meanings by completing the sentences that follow. Use as many terms as you can think of in your answers, but don't include *happy*. If you need to, look up the word *hapless* also.

a. Happy comes from the Middle English word __________, which means __________.

b. The opposite of *unhappy* is __________.

c. The opposite of *hapless* is __________.

Group Discussion

Name_________________________ Class______________ Date______________

6. Which word—*unhappy* or *hapless*—do you think is a better antonym for the word *happy* as the speaker uses it in section 3? Give evidence for your response.

____

____

____

____

7. What is the effect of the speaker's repetition of the term *happy* in section 3?

____

____

____

____

RL.11–12.4
L.11–12.5, a

Figures of Speech—Paradox A paradox is a situation or statement that appears to be impossible or contradictory but is true.

8. How do the paradoxes that follow reinforce the theme of Keats's ode?

a. Heard melodies are sweet, but those unheard
Are sweeter…

____

____

____

____

____

Name________________________ Class____________ Date____________

b. Bold lover, never, never canst thou kiss,
Though winning near the goal—yet, do not grieve;
She cannot fade, though thou hast not thy bliss,
Forever wilt thou love and she be fair!

Group Discussion

Name______________________________ Class______________ Date______________

ASSIGN

SL.11–12.4
SL.11–12.1 b, c

Meet with your literature group to plan your discussion. Each group member should become the expert on one or more of the questions answered on pages 34–37. Each expert will then guide the discussion on his or her question(s). List each group member and the question(s) he or she will become an expert on in the chart that follows.

Group Member	Question(s) to Present

To become an expert, spend some extra time thinking about your question(s) and consulting the text for relevant details. Building on your question(s), write down one or two discussion points or related questions for group members to consider as they explore text issues.

____

____

____

____

____

____

Name ______________________ Class __________ Date __________

DISCUSS

SL.11–12.1, a–d

Break into your assigned literature group to conduct your discussion. The expert for question 1 should begin by reading aloud the question and leading the discussion in response. Follow this process for each question until you have covered them all.

Remember that literature groups contain room for disagreement. Healthy debate can help all members push their understanding to a new level. Use your time wisely so that you are able to discuss all the questions sufficiently.

In your discussion, follow the guidelines that follow.

Discussion Guidelines

- Come to discussions prepared; be sure you have carefully and thoroughly answered all questions.
- Express your ideas clearly. When presenting on your question and commenting on others, support your ideas with concrete evidence from the text. Give specific page numbers.
- Work with your group to promote civil, democratic discussions and decision making.
- Work with your group to set clear goals and deadlines.
- Establish individual roles as needed (e.g., note taker, moderator, etc.).
- Propel conversations by posing and responding to questions that probe reasoning and evidence.
- Ensure a hearing for a full range of positions on a topic or issue; clarify, verify, or challenge ideas and conclusions; and promote divergent and creative perspectives.
- Respond thoughtfully to diverse perspectives and synthesize comments, claims, and evidence made on all sides of an issue.
- Resolve contradictions when possible and determine what additional information or research is required to deepen the investigation or complete the task.

At the end of your discussion, be prepared to share the insights you have gained with your class. On the lines that follow, briefly summarize the most interesting ideas or insights you heard or experienced during the discussion.

____

____

____

____

____

____

Name________________________ Class____________ Date____________

Ode on a Grecian Urn
John Keats

21st Century Skills Project **Multimedia Poem**

Now that you have analyzed and discussed the poem in detail, you will have the opportunity to extend your thinking about it creatively by writing a poem of your own. Your assignment is to write a poem about a work of art. If resources allow, you can publish your poem online.

21st Century Skills Project

PART 1 Write a Poem

Using "Ode on a Grecian Urn" as a model, write a poem about a work of art. In your poem, you should both present the work using the resources of poetic language and develop a theme related to the meaning and value of the work as you see it. If you publish your poem online later, you'll be able to add links to pictures and other media to help elaborate on the images and details in your poem. Keep this in mind as you write.

To help you plan your poem, answer the questions that follow.

1. What work of art will I write about? What is its title?

____

____

2. What is the work about? What does it present or represent?

____

____

____

____

Name______________________ Class__________ Date__________

3. What do I find meaningful or valuable about this work of art?

____

____

____

4. Why do I care about this work of art? Why should the readers of my poem?

____

____

____

____

5. What characteristics does this particular art form have? Can I use them to add depth to my presentation?.

____

____

____

____

6. What is my creative concept for this poem? (Keats's creative concept could be described like this: To write an ode describing the images painted on an urn, explaining their artistic value, and exploring the metaphorical meaning of the fact that the images are action frozen in time.)

____

____

____

____

21st Century Skills Project

Name__________________________________ Class____________ Date____________

7. What elements of poetry and poetic language can I use to express what I want to say about this work of art? Write your responses in the chart below.

IDEAS AND LANGUAGE FOR MY POEM ABOUT A WORK OF ART

Poetic Element	Ideas or Language	Connection to Art Work
Word Choice		
Figurative Language		
Imagery		
Sound Devices		
Rhythm and Meter		
Structure		

W.11–12.5 **Freewrite** Before you begin drafting your poem, you might find it helpful to freewrite what you want to say in prose. Focus on getting all your thoughts down without editing yourself. After you've written what you want to say, go back and highlight key images and vivid descriptions that would work well in your poem.

Name_________________________ Class____________ Date____________

Draft As you write your poem, keep the following tips in mind:

- Begin drafting by writing the opening lines of your poem. Ideally, your first lines should identify the work of art you're writing about and establish your poetic voice.
- Choose your words carefully. Use vivid, concrete images that appeal to the senses and make sure your images and figurative language communicate your desired tone.
- Convey your ideas as precisely as possible and avoid unnecessary words.
- If you're using stanzas, each one should convey a cohesive idea and these ideas should progress or flow from one stanza to the next. Consider saving your most powerful image for your final stanza or last line.
- Make sure your ending provides a sense of completion to the poem and that it is consistent with the message you've been conveying throughout.
- After you're done, choose a title for your poem.

Present Your Poem If you are not going on to Part 2 of the 21st Century Skills Project, your teacher may ask you to present your poem orally as the completion of the project. You may also be evaluated on the presentation.

Before you present your poem to the class, practice reading it aloud on your own and in front of family members or friends. Don't rush your reading. Use your punctuation and line breaks to help you determine when to pause. Speak clearly and look at your audience. Try to memorize some, if not all, of your poem so that you don't have to read throughout your presentation. Vary your intonation to get your meaning across and to emphasize certain words or ideas.

Name_________________________ Class_____________ Date_____________

PART 2 Publish Online

W.11–12.6
SL.11–12.5

After you've finished Part 1 of this project, publish your poem online in an interactive format that includes an audio recording of your poem and hyperlinks to images and other visual media (such as video clips).

SL.11–12.6

Audio Recording Before you record your poem, practice reading it aloud. Don't rush as you read. Use your punctuation and line breaks to determine where to pause. Be sure to adapt your speech to the context. For example, if your poem is written using relatively formal language, don't read it with an informal tone of voice. When you feel prepared, record your poem.

Links to Visual Media When you publish your poem, you will include hyperlinks to visual media, which will elaborate on the images and details you've included in your poem. These links will help your readers get a better understanding of the work of art you wrote about. For example, if you wrote a poem about a painting, you should try to include an image of the painting. If you wrote a poem about a short story by James Joyce, you might want to include images of Dublin or of situations like those in the story. You could also include a video clip from a film version of the story. Be sure to position the hyperlinks as close as possible to what they go with. Pay attention to copyright information when you choose your media. Include credit information if you need to.

Before you publish your poem, fill in the chart that follows to help you decide what images and/or other media you want to link to.

Image or Concept in Poem	Line Number(s)	Corresponding Visual Media Link

21st Century Skills Project

Name ______________________ Class __________ Date __________

W.11–12.6

Publish and Present After you've completed your chart, decide where you will publish your poem. If your school already has a Web site for student work, you might consider publishing your poem there. You can also search online for Web sites that allow you to create your own page for free. This type of site often provides templates and is easy to use.

Publish your poem on your chosen site. Using your chart as a guide, hyperlink various images in your poem to photos, fine art, and other media. Add a hyperlink to your audio recording at the beginning of the poem. When you're finished, send the URL of your site to your teacher and classmates so they can read and view your work.

After you've completed this project, answer the following questions:

1. How does your audio recording add to the presentation of your poem?

____

____

____

____

2. Which images and concepts in your poem led to the most interesting links? Why?

____

____

____

____

3. What would you change in the planning, creation, and presentation of this project if you were to do it again?

____

____

____

____

Name________________________ Class____________ Date____________

SL.11–12.1, b, c, d

Evaluate Read your classmates' poems once without clicking on any of the links so that you understand the content of the poems. Then read the poems a second time and click on the links to see the media and hear the audio recording. As you read and view your classmates' work, take notes about the content and effectiveness of their poems and visual media. Then use your notes to participate in a class discussion about the project.

1. How well does the poem present the work of art it is about? Explain.

____

____

____

____

2. Does the audio recording add to or detract from the poem? Explain.

____

____

____

____

3. How well do the links connect to images and concepts in the poem? Explain.

____

____

____

____

4. What would you add or change in the poem or the accompanying visual media? Why?

____

____

____

____

21st Century Skills Project

Name________________________________ Class_______________ Date_______________

Group Discussion

Oliver Twist

Charles Dickens

Glencoe Literature, pages 942–948

RL.11–12.10

Before starting the lesson, read the following selection and complete the lesson activities in ***Glencoe Literature: British Literature.***

from *Oliver Twist* **(pages 942–948)**

In this lesson you will analyze and discuss an excerpt from Dickens's novel *Oliver Twist*. You will then plan and create a slide show in which you compare and contrast two interpretations of Dickens's story: the musical *Oliver* and a film version of your choosing. Through your participation in the discussion and your work on the project, you will practice the following standards:

RL.11–12.4
RL.11–12.6

Craft and Structure

- Determine the meanings of words and phrases as they are used in the text
- Analyze a case in which grasping point of view requires distinguishing what is directly stated from what is really meant.

RL.11–12.7

Integration of Knowledge and Ideas

- Analyze and evaluate multiple interpretations of a story

Group Discussion

Discussing literature within a small group can help you grow as a reader and as a member of a learning community. Together, you and other group members can arrive at a better understanding of a selection, its ideas and craft, and its connection to other works and areas of study.

PLAN

RL.11–12.1
W.11–12.9, a
W.11–12.10
L.11–12.1
L.11–12.2, b

To prepare for discussion, build your content knowledge by examining the novel excerpt in greater detail. If possible, read the entire text or selected portions of *Oliver Twist*. On your own, write your answers to the questions that follow using text evidence. You may also write additional questions about the selection that you wish to discuss with your group. Your teacher may review your answers before the discussion, so be sure to use correct grammar, spelling, punctuation, and capitalization.

Name________________________ Class____________ Date____________

RL.11–12.6 **Point of View** Point of view in narrative fiction refers to the standpoint from which the story is told. In a story with **third-person omniscient** point of view, like *Oliver Twist*, the narrator stands outside the story and describes the characters and actions from an all-knowing perspective. That is, the narrator can describe character's unspoken thoughts and feelings and knows the truth about circumstances and events, even when none of the characters do.

Although not a participant in the story, an omniscient narrator will usually show a special awareness of and sympathy for the thoughts and feelings of the main character(s). The narrator may also reveal an attitude that is different from that of any character or even from his or her own direct statements through the use of

- **sarcasm:** biting, often ironic language that is used to express disapproval or frustration (Example: *I guess that's my fault, too, just like everything else.*)
- **verbal irony:** language that expresses the opposite meaning from what is actually stated (Example: *Since you gave my paper an F-, I guess you really loved it.*)
- **understatement:** language, often ironic, that downplays something to an absurd degree (Example: *Since you gave my paper an F-, I guess there was something you didn't like about it.*)

1. In the excerpt from *Oliver Twist*, how does the narrator reveal an all-knowing awareness of circumstances and events?

____

____

____

____

2. How does the narrator show that his perspective on events is strongly sympathetic toward that of Oliver himself?

____

____

____

____

Name________________________ Class__________ Date__________

3. How does the narrator use the devices of sarcasm, irony, or understatement to convey a meaning different from what is directly stated? Write your responses in the graphic organizers that follow. Make additional copies of this page if you need to.

Page________

Direct Statement	Literal Meaning
Device	**Real Meaning**

Page________

Direct Statement	Literal Meaning
Device	**Real Meaning**

Page________

Direct Statement	Literal Meaning
Device	**Real Meaning**

Page________

Direct Statement	Literal Meaning
Device	**Real Meaning**

Name______________________ Class__________ Date__________

RL.11–12.4 **Word Choice** One clue to a discrepancy between what the narrator says and what the narrator means can be **diction**, or word choice. In addition to their denotative, or dictionary meanings, words can be chosen for their figurative meanings, connotations, and multiple meanings.

4. How does the narrator's choice of words and phrases help to convey his ironic tone? In the chart that follows, cite specific examples from the text by page number and explain each one's contribution.

Figurative Meaning	Connotation	Multiple Meanings

Name________________________ Class__________ Date__________

Group Discussion

5. Based on the passages you cited for questions 3 and 4 and on your reading of the rest of the excerpt, how would you describe the narrator's real attitude toward

a. Oliver and his request for more gruel?

____

____

____

b. Mr. Bumble and the Members of the Board?

____

____

____

c. the Poor Laws of England?

____

____

____

Name ______________________ Class __________ Date __________

ASSIGN

SL.11–12.1, a, b

Meet with your literature group to plan your discussion. Each group member should become the expert on one or more of the questions or question parts answered on pages 48–51. Each expert will then guide the discussion on his or her question(s). List each group member and the question(s) he or she will become an expert on in the chart below.

Group Member	Question(s) to Present

To become an expert on your question(s), spend some extra time thinking about your question(s) and consulting the text for relevant details. Building on your question, write down one or two discussion points or related questions for group members to consider as they explore text issues.

____

____

____

____

____

____

Name________________ Class________ Date________

DISCUSS

SL.11–12.1, a–d

Break into your assigned literature group to conduct your discussion. The expert for question 1 should begin by reading aloud the question and leading the discussion in response. Follow this process for each question until you have covered them all.

Remember that literature groups contain room for disagreement. Healthy debate can help all members push their understanding to a new level. Use your time wisely so that you are able to discuss all the questions sufficiently.

In your discussion, follow the guidelines below.

Discussion Guidelines

- Come to discussions prepared; be sure you have carefully and thoroughly answered all questions.
- Express your ideas clearly. When presenting on your question and commenting on others, support your ideas with concrete evidence from the text. Give specific page numbers.
- Work with your group to promote civil, democratic discussions and decision making.
- Work with your group to set clear goals and deadlines.
- Establish individual roles as needed (e.g., note taker, moderator, etc.).
- Propel conversations by posing and responding to questions that probe reasoning and evidence.
- Ensure a hearing for a full range of positions on a topic or issue; clarify, verify, or challenge ideas and conclusions; and promote divergent and creative perspectives.
- Respond thoughtfully to diverse perspectives and synthesize comments, claims, and evidence made on all sides of an issue.
- Resolve contradictions when possible and determine what additional information or research is required to deepen the investigation or complete the task.

At the end of your discussion, be prepared to share the insights you have gained with your class. On the lines below, briefly summarize the most interesting ideas or insights you heard or experienced during the discussion.

Name ____________________ Class __________ Date __________

Oliver Twist
Charles Dickens

21st Century Skills Project **Slide Show**

Now that you have analyzed and discussed the scene depicted in the novel excerpt in detail, you will have the opportunity to extend your thinking about it creatively by completing a group project. Your assignment is to compare two interpretations of this scene in two other versions of the story: the musical *Oliver* and any of the several film versions of the story. In carrying out this project, you will follow the steps below:

- View a live or recorded production of the musical *Oliver*.
- View a film version of *Oliver Twist*.
- Gather examples and organize and write commentary to compare, contrast, and evaluate the two interpretations.
- If resources allow, you can use your examples and commentary to create and present a slide show.

PART 1 Compare and Contrast Interpretations

RL.11–12.7 SL.11–12.1, a–d

With a small group, discuss your impressions and opinions of the two new interpretations of the scene in which Oliver asks for more gruel. Decide which of the two interpretations you think more effectively captures the spirit of Dickens's narrative version and why. Use your answers to this question to create an outline showing the different aspects of the interpretations that you will compare and contrast in your slide show. You may want to focus on aspects of the story such as characterization, conflict, dialogue, and narration, or you may want to look closely at elements introduced by the new genres (such as the musical numbers in *Oliver* or film techniques in the movie version).

W.11–12.7

Find Examples For each aspect you wish to compare and contrast, assemble supporting examples such as images, sound recordings, transcriptions of dialogue, or other relevant elements of the interpretations. Assign each of your examples a number so that you can easily find it again. Then write commentary to go with each example, explaining how it develops and supports your comparison and evaluation. Use the chart that follows to help you categorize and record your findings.

Name________________________________ Class______________ Date______________

Aspect of the Interpretations to Compare and Contrast	*Oliver*, the Musical	*Oliver Twist*: Film Version Director: ____________ Year Produced: ________

21st Century Skills Project

Name________________________ Class______________ Date______________

Organize After you complete the chart, consider how you'd like to organize your examples and commentary. Do you want to address one aspect of the interpretations at a time, or do you want to address all of the examples related to one interpretation? Keep in mind that your commentary and images are meant to be a part of a slide show. This means that the information and images need to flow together logically.

Create Slides Decide which group members will be responsible for creating each slide or group of slides. Mock-up each slide on a sheet of paper or poster board. Use your chart of examples as a guide.

- **Examples** You can indicate the example on each slide with a brief description or rough sketch. If possible, print out images or other examples and attach them to the slide they go with.
- **Commentary** Add your commentary on the example to each slide. Remember not to overload a slide with too much text. Use bulleted lists and headings to make your commentary reader-friendly.
- **Additional Slides** Include a title slide for your presentation. You may want also to include slides to indicate transitions or divisions between sections. as needed to help your viewers follow the steps of your presentation. Create a concluding slide or slides to summarize your points and to leave the viewer with something to think about.

After all the content is written, review each other's work and make sure each presentation flows together well and conveys the similarities and differences between the two interpretations, as well as your evaluation of them. Remember to credit your image sources.

Present Your Commentary If you are not going on to Part 2 of the 21st Century Skills Project, your teacher may ask you to present your mocked-up slides as the end result of the project. You may also be evaluated on the presentation.

Name________________________ Class______________ Date______________

PART 2 Present a Slide Show

SL.11–12.4
SL.11–12.5

After you've finished Part 1 of this project, create your slide show. Make sure your examples and commentary are visually appealing, clearly presented, and flow together logically. Be sure to make strategic use of digital media to enhance your presentation.

Rehearse your slide show in front of friends or family members before presenting to your class. Make sure that each person in your group knows which portions of the presentation he or she is responsible for. As you rehearse, make sure the transitions between presenters are smooth.

After you've completed this project, answer the following questions.

1. How well does your slide show compare and contrast the two interpretations? How well does it convey your evaluation of them?

____
____
____
____

2. Does your slide show flow well? Is information presented clearly? Explain.

____
____
____
____

3. What would you change in the planning, creation, and presentation of this project if you were to do it again?

____
____
____
____

Name ______________________ Class __________ Date __________

SL.11–12.1, b, c, d

Evaluate As you view your classmates' work, take notes about the content and effectiveness of their slide shows. Then use your notes to participate in a class discussion about the project.

1. Do the comparisons and contrasts of the examples make sense? Explain.

2. Is the information in the slide show presented clearly and effectively? Explain.

3. What would you add or change in the slide show? Why? Consider content and organization.

21st Century Skills Project

Name________________________ Class____________ Date____________

Group Discussion

Araby

James Joyce

British Literature, pages 1094–1101

RL.11–12.10

Before starting the lesson, read the following selection and complete the lesson activities in ***British, Literature.***

"Araby" **(pages 1094–1101)**

In this lesson you will analyze and discuss James Joyce's short story "Araby." You will then write a screenplay based on the story. If resources allow, you will film your screenplay. Through your participation in the discussion and your work on the project, you will practice the following standards:

RL.11–12.3

Key Ideas and Details

- Analyze the impact of the author's choices regarding how to develop and relate character.

RL.11–12.5
RL.11–12.6

Craft and Structure

- Analyze plot structure.
- Analyze point of view that requires distinguishing what is directly stated from what is really meant.

Group Discussion

Discussing literature within a small group can help you grow as a reader and as a member of a learning community. Together, you and other group members can arrive at a better understanding of a selection, its ideas and craft, and its connection to other works and areas of study.

PLAN

RL.11–12.1
W.11–12.9, a
W.11–12.10
L.11–12.1
L.11–12.2, b

To prepare for discussion, build your content knowledge by examining the selection in greater detail. On your own, write your answers to the questions that follow using text evidence. You may also write additional questions about the selection that you wish to discuss with your group. Your teacher may review your answers before the discussion, so be sure to use correct grammar, spelling, punctuation, and capitalization.

Name _______________ Class _______________ Date _______________

RL.11–12.5 **Plot Structure** The sequence of events in a narrative work is called plot. Most short stories have a single plot line and are tightly crafted to build suspense. A plot line usually consists of the following elements:

EXPOSITION → RISING ACTION → CLIMAX → FALLING ACTION → RESOLUTION

1. Does Joyce's story fit this pattern? Identify these five stages of the plot in "Araby." Write your responses in the following graphic organizer. Note also any ways in which Joyce's story seems to differ from the usual pattern.

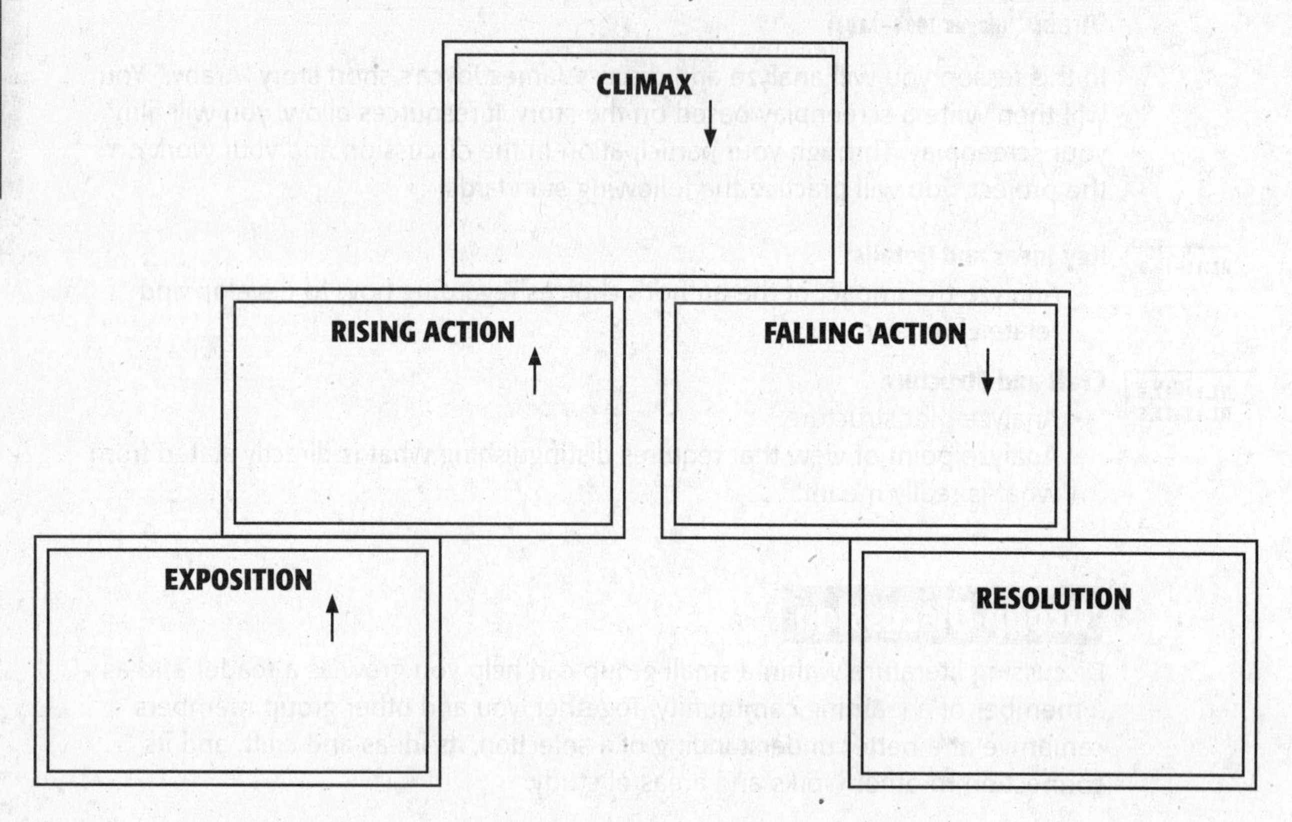

2. In what ways does "Araby" seem not to fit into this traditional structure? What impact does this difference in structure have on the story's meaning and aesthetic impact?

____

____

____

____

Name ______________________ Class ____________ Date ______________

RL.11–12.3 **Characterization** The process by which an author develops character is called characterization. Authors develop character through action, dialogue, and narrative commentary. Well-developed characters, like real people, are often complex rather than simple. Complex characters usually have internal as well as external conflict and multiple or conflicting motivations. **External conflict** results from circumstances or the actions of others characters. **Internal conflict** results from mixed or divided feelings, beliefs, goals, or values.

3. How would you describe the external conflict of the first-person narrator?

____

____

____

____

4. How would you describe the narrator's internal conflict?

____

____

____

____

5. Complex behavior often contains both positive and negative elements. In what ways do you find the following behaviors of the boy likeable or admirable? In what ways can you see the same behaviors as flawed or risky? Write your responses in the following graphic organizer.

LIKEABLE	← BEHAVIOR →	FLAWED
	a. Falling in love with Mangan's Sister	
	b. Watching her door and following her	
	c. Promising to bring her something from the bazaar	
	d. Losing interest in everything except the bazaar	
	e. Persisting in his determination to go to the bazaar despite setbacks	

Group Discussion

Name________________________________ Class______________ Date______________

Group Discussion

RL.11–12.6 **Point of View** Point of view in narrative fiction refers to the standpoint from which the story is told. In a story with **first-person** point of view, like "Araby," the narrator is a character in the story and uses the words *I* and *me*. At a deeper level, point of view can also be understood as the narrator's way of looking at the world and at what happens in the story. Sometimes the narrator's viewpoint is revealed indirectly through meaning that is different from what is stated directly.

1. In what ways do you think the narrator's understanding or attitude regarding the events of the story might be different from that he had as a boy during the time he is telling about? What evidence can you find in the story for this difference? Write your responses in the following chart for the events or characters indicated.

a. Mangan's Sister

Viewpoint of the Boy at the Time of the Story	Narrator's Adult Viewpoint	Text Evidence

b. The Uncle's Behavior

Viewpoint of the Boy at the Time of the Story	Narrator's Adult Viewpoint	Text Evidence

Name ______________________ Class ____________ Date ____________

c. The Bazaar

Viewpoint of the Boy at the Time of the Story	Narrator's Adult Viewpoint	Text Evidence

d. The Boy's "Epiphany" or Insight

Viewpoint of the Boy at the Time of the Story	Narrator's Adult Viewpoint	Text Evidence

RL.11–12.5 **Resolution** The resolution of a story consists of the actions, events, and insights that bring the conflict to an end and/or enable the protagonist to move on.

5. In your own words, describe how the central conflicts in "Araby" are resolved. Do you find this an aesthetically satisfying resolution to the story? Why or why not?

____

____

____

____

____

Group Discussion

Name________________________ Class____________ Date____________

ASSIGN

RL.11–12.5
SL.11–12.1, a, b, d

Meet with your literature group to plan your discussion. Each group member should become the expert on one or more of the questions or question parts answered on pages 60–63. Each expert will then guide the discussion on his or her question(s). List each group member and the question(s) he or she will become an expert on in the chart below.

Group Member	Question(s) to Present

To become an expert on your question(s), spend some extra time thinking about your question(s) and consulting the text for relevant details. Building on your question(s), write down one or two discussion points or related questions for group members to consider as they explore text issues.

____

____

____

____

____

____

Name________________________________ Class____________ Date____________

DISCUSS

SL.11–12.1, a–d

Break into your assigned literature group to conduct your discussion. The expert for question 1 should begin by reading aloud the question and leading the discussion in response. Follow this process for each question until you have covered them all.

Remember that literature groups contain room for disagreement. Healthy debate can help all members push their understanding to a new level. Use your time wisely so that you are able to discuss all the questions sufficiently.

In your discussion, follow the guidelines below.

Discussion Guidelines

- Come to discussions prepared; be sure you have carefully and thoroughly answered all questions.
- Express your ideas clearly. When presenting on your question and commenting on others, support your ideas with concrete evidence from the text. Give specific page numbers.
- Work with your group to promote civil, democratic discussions and decision making.
- Work with your group to set clear goals and deadlines.
- Establish individual roles as needed (e.g., note taker, moderator, etc.).
- Propel conversations by posing and responding to questions that probe reasoning and evidence.
- Ensure a hearing for a full range of positions on a topic or issue; clarify, verify, or challenge ideas and conclusions; and promote divergent and creative perspectives.
- Respond thoughtfully to diverse perspectives and synthesize comments, claims, and evidence made on all sides of an issue.
- Resolve contradictions when possible and determine what additional information or research is required to deepen the investigation or complete the task.

At the end of your discussion, be prepared to share the insights you have gained with your class. On the lines below, briefly summarize the most interesting ideas or insights you heard or experienced during the discussion.

____

____

____

____

____

____

Name________________________ Class____________ Date____________

Araby

James Joyce

21st Century Skills Project **Movie**

Now that you have analyzed and discussed the story in detail, you will have the opportunity to extend your thinking about it creatively by participating in a group project. Your assignment is to write a screenplay based on the story. If resources allow, turn your screenplay into a movie and present it to your classmates and teacher.

PART 1 Write a Screenplay

W.11–12.5

With a small group, write a screenplay based on "Araby." Before you begin writing, answer the following questions to help guide you. You may want to make a photocopy of the story for your group to mark up and make additional notes on.

1. What "take" or interpretation of Joyce's story do you want to bring out in your movie version? (You may want to return to this question after considering the ones that follow, but keep it in mind as your proceed.)

____

____

____

____

2. Which parts of the dialogue in the story will you include? What alterations or additions will you need to make?

____

____

____

____

Name______________________________ Class______________ Date______________

3. How will your portray the different characters and settings of the story? Write your responses in the chart below. In Column 1, describe the physical resources (actors, sets, props, costumes, sound, and lighting) you will need for each one. In Column 2, describe the film resources (shot composition, camera techniques, film-editing strategies, sound overlay, special effects) you would like to use.

"Araby"—The Movie	Physical Resources	Film Resources
Setting **Narrator's House** **Main Characters** **The Narrator** **The Uncle** **The Aunt**		
Setting **The Street** **Main Characters** **The Narrator** **Mangan's Sister**		
Setting **The Bazaar** **Main Characters** **The Narrator** **The Young Lady**		

4. How will you film information that we get directly from the narrator about his thoughts and feelings at the time of the story? Some possibilities are listed below and on the next page, but you may come up with other ideas.

- Voiceover narration
- Additional dialogue or spoken lines
- Close-ups and other camera techniques

21st Century Skills Project

Name________________________________ Class____________ Date____________

- Facial expressions and other physical actions
- Special visual or sound effects

____

____

____

____

____

____

Following is a list of cinematography terms that may be helpful as you develop your screenplay.

Cinematography Terms	
Camera Techniques	**Editing Techniques**
Frame (the arrangement of objects within the boundary of the film image) Camera Angle high angle (looking down) low angle (looking up) Camera Movement pan (rotate right or left, up or down) track (move in a straight line) Shot Distance close-up two-shot (two heads in frame) medium shot long or distant shot	Cut (immediate change to a new shot) Jump Cut (cut to a shot that shows a new time or place) Fade (gradual change to/from blank frame) fade to black fade out fade in Sequence (series of shots in one scene) Point of View Shot (cut to a shot that represents what is seen by a character introduced in a previous shot)

Name ____________________ Class __________ Date __________

Use the following student model to help you format your screenplay.

Long shot of Oliver, as the other boys look on, walking with his bowl held out before him toward the master, who stands with his arms folded, a frown of disapproval on his face.

Cut to close-up of Master's face from the side.

Cut to a medium shot of the other boys waiting at the table. The camera pans across their breathless, waiting faces as the master speaks.

MASTER

(coldly)

May I help you?

Cut to high-angle point-of-view close-up of Oliver's frightened but determined face.

OLIVER

(quietly and very politely)

Please, sir, I want some more.

Cut to low-angle point-of-view close-up of the Master, whose jaw hangs open with astonishment.

MASTER

(faintly)

What?

Cut back to high-angle close-up of Oliver, who looks even more frightened but still determined to carry out his mission.

OLIVER

(in a voice so quiet it is almost a whisper)

Please, sir, I want some more.

Cut to medium shot from the side as the Master swings his ladle at Oliver's head and barely misses. Oliver ducks and turns to run away but the Master grabs him from behind and holds him tightly.

MASTER

(shrieking wildly)

Beadle! Beadle!

Name________________ Class________ Date________

Present Your Screenplay If you are not going on to Part 2 of the 21st Century Skills Project, your teacher may ask you to present your screenplay as the final product of the project. You may also be evaluated on the presentation.

In presenting your screenplay you may choose to assign parts and act out a couple of key scenes. If you have voiceover narration, one person may need to read those lines, while another reads the stage and cinematography directions. You may also want to include some props and scenery.

PART 2 Film a Movie Version of "Araby"

SL.11–12.1, b

After your group has finished Part 1 of this project, you can begin to create your film. Decide whether you will film the entire story or only a key scene or two from it. With your group, answer the questions below to help plan the filming of your movie.

1. What scene or scenes from the story will we film?

____

____

____

____

2. What location(s) will we use to film our movie? Why?

____

____

____

____

3. Who will play each part in the movie? How will we make the casting decisions?

____

____

____

____

Name______________________ Class__________ Date__________

4. What scenery, props, and costumes will we need?

____

____

____

____

5. What type of music and sound effects do we want to include? What equipment will we need to do this?

____

____

____

____

6. What filming and editing techniques will help us bring out the aspects of the story we want to emphasize? Why?

____

____

____

____

____

7. What type of video editing software will we use?

____

____

8. List the members of your group and the tasks each person will complete. Some tasks will need the help of more than one person.

Name	Tasks

Present Your Movie After you've filmed and edited your movie, review it for its content, creativity, group work, and communication of ideas. If you have time, make changes to your movie to strengthen any areas that seem weak. Then present it to the class.

After you've shown your movie to your class, answer the following questions with your group.

1. What worked well in your movie and why?

____

____

____

____

2. What would you change in the planning, creation, and presentation of this movie if you were to do this project again?

____

____

____

____

Name________________ **Class**________ **Date**________

SL.11–12.1, b, c, d
SL.11–12.2

Observe and Evaluate As you view your classmates' movies, take notes about the content and effectiveness of their films. Then use your notes to participate in a class discussion about the films.

1. How well does the movie convey the events of the story? Explain.

2. Is the presentation of the narrator's internal dialogue, ideas, and feelings effective? Explain.

3. How effectively do the filming and editing techniques present and interpret the resolution of the story?

4. What would you add or change in the film? Why?

Reading Lessons: Informational Text

Name_______________ Class__________ Date__________

from A Distant Mirror

Barbara Tuchman

Glencoe Literature: British Literature, pages 185–187

RI.11–12.10 Before starting the lesson, read the following selections and complete the lesson activities in ***Glencoe Literature: British Literature.***

from *A Distant Mirror* **(pages 185–187)**

In this lesson you will analyze and discuss an excerpt from the National Book Award winning historical study *A Distant Mirror.* You will then create a multimedia exhibit documentary on chivalry. Through your participation in the discussion and your work on the project, you will practice the following standards:

RI.11–12.2 **Key Ideas and Details**

- Determine two or more central ideas of a text.
- Analyze their development, including how they interact and build on one another to provide a complex analysis.
- Provide an objective summary of the text.

RI.11–12.7 **Integration of Knowledge and Ideas**

- Integrate and evaluate multiple sources of information presented in different media or formats as well as in words in order to address a question or solve a problem.

Group Discussion

Discussing nonfiction within a small group can help you grow as a reader and as a member of a learning community. Together, you and other group members can arrive at a better understanding of a selection, its ideas and craft, and its connection to other works and areas of study.

PLAN

RI.11–12.1
W.11–12.9, b
W.11–12.10
L.11–12.1
L.11–12.2, b

To prepare for discussion, build your content knowledge by examining the selection in greater detail. On your own, write your answers to the questions that follow, using text evidence. You may also write additional questions about the selection that you wish to discuss with your group. Your teacher may review your answers before the discussion, so be sure to use correct grammar, spelling, punctuation, and capitalization.

Group Discussion

Name________________________ Class____________ Date____________

RI.11–12.2 **Main Ideas** The main ideas in a work of nonfiction are the messages that the author wants to convey by writing. Usually the author makes the significance of these ideas clear by developing them against the backdrop of the reader's previous experience, beliefs, or assumptions about the topic. The author then supports the main ideas with details, which could be sub-ideas, reasoning, or evidence. When you **summarize** a text, you explain the main ideas and the most important details.

1. What background experiences, beliefs, or assumptions does the author think her readers are likely to have concerning chivalry?

____

____

____

____

2. What do you think is the most important idea the author wants to get across in the excerpt? Based on your answer to question 1, how do you think the average reader is likely to respond to this idea? Explain.

____

____

____

____

3. What is another main idea the author wants to get across? How do you think the average reader is likely to respond to this idea? Explain.

____

____

____

____

Group Discussion

Name________________ Class__________ Date__________

4. Describe the development of the two ideas you have identified over the course of the excerpt. How do they interact and build on one another to provide a complex analysis? Write your responses in the graphic organizer that follows.

Idea 1:		Idea 2:
Development	→ Interaction ←	Development

Group Discussion

Name______________________ Class______________ Date______________

5. In your own words, provide an objective summary of the excerpt.

____

____

____

____

____

____

Group Discussion

Name____________________ Class__________ Date__________

ASSIGN

SL.11–12.1, a, b

Meet with your literature group to plan your discussion. Each group member should become the expert on one of the questions answered on pages 77-80. Each expert will then guide the discussion on his or her question. List each group member and his or her question in the chart below.

Group Member	Question(s) to Present

To become an expert on your question, spend some extra time thinking about it and consulting the text for relevant details. Building on your question, write down one or two discussion points or related questions for group members to consider as they explore text issues.

____

____

____

____

____

____

Name ____________________ Class __________ Date __________

DISCUSS

SL.11–12.1 a, c, d
SL.11–12.3
SL.11–12.4
L.11–12.1
L.11–12.3

Break into your assigned literature group to conduct your discussion. The expert for question 1 should begin by reading aloud the question and leading the discussion in response. Follow this process for each question until you have covered them all.

Remember that literature groups contain room for disagreement. Healthy debate can help all members push their understanding to a new level. Use your time wisely so that you are able to discuss all the questions sufficiently.

In your discussion, follow the guidelines below.

Discussion Guidelines

- Come to discussions prepared; be sure you have carefully and thoroughly answered all questions.
- Express your ideas clearly. When presenting on your question and commenting on others, support your ideas with concrete evidence from the text. Give specific page numbers.
- Work with your group to promote civil, democratic discussions and decision making.
- Work with your group to set clear goals and deadlines.
- Establish individual roles as needed (i.e., note taker, moderator, etc.).
- Propel conversations by posing and responding to questions that probe reasoning and evidence.
- Ensure a hearing for a full range of positions on a topic or issue; clarify, verify, or challenge ideas and conclusions; and promote divergent and creative perspectives.
- Respond thoughtfully to diverse perspectives and synthesize comments, claims, and evidence made on all sides of an issue.
- Resolve contradictions when possible and determine what additional information or research is required to deepen the investigation or complete the task.

At the end of your discussion, be prepared to share the insights you have gained with your class. On the lines below, briefly summarize the most interesting ideas or insights you heard or experienced during the discussion.

____

____

____

____

____

____

Name____________________ Class____________ Date____________

from A Distant Mirror

Barbara Tuchman

21st Century Skills Project Multimedia Exhibit

Now that you have analyzed and discussed the essay in detail, you will have the opportunity to extend your thinking about it creatively by completing a group project. Your assignment is to develop a proposal for a multimedia exhibit that explores chivalry during the European middle ages. In carrying out this project, you will follow the steps below:

- Conduct research into the history of chivalry.
- Organize and write content for a multimedia exhibit proposal.
- If resources allow, you create and present your multimedia exhibit.

PART 1 Develop a Multimedia Exhibit Proposal

With a small group, decide which aspect of chivalry you would like to research. Narrow your topic enough to make it manageable, but make sure it is broad and important enough to be worthwhile and likely to yield lots of interesting information. One way to narrow your topic appropriately is to organize your research around a significant question or set of related questions that you would like to answer. Write your question(s) below.

____

____

____

____

____

Assign Research Use your question(s) to create a list of research tasks and assignments for members of your group.

Member: ____________ Assignment: ____________

Member: ____________ Assignment: ____________

Member: ____________ Assignment: ____________

Member: ____________ Assignment: ____________

Member: ____________ Assignment: ____________

21st Century Skills Project

Name ________________ Class ________ Date ________

W.11–12.7
W.11–12.8
SL.11–12.2

Conduct Research Using your question(s) as a guide, gather relevant information from multiple authoritative print and digital sources. Assess the strengths and limitations of each source in terms of the task, purpose, and audience. Record your findings in the organizers below or on note cards. Make additional copies of this page as needed to complete the assignment.

Aspect of Chivalry	Relevant Information
Source Information	**Source Assessment**

Aspect of Chivalry	Relevant Information
Source Information	**Source Assessment**

Aspect of Chivalry	Relevant Information
Source Information	**Source Assessment**

Aspect of Chivalry	Relevant Information
Source Information	**Source Assessment**

21st Century Skills Project

Name________________________ Class__________ Date__________

W.11–12.6

Organize Information After you've finished conducting research, you'll need to organize your exhibit proposal with your group. First, based on what you've learned, turn the answer(s) to your research question(s) into a main idea or thesis. Then identify which aspects of chivalry you'll focus on in your proposal to support this thesis; what kinds of images, video, sound, or other media you'll include; and how these media will be arranged. Use the graphic organizer below to help you organize your content.

Title of Exhibit:

Main Idea of Exhibit:

Aspect of Chivalry	Supporting Media

RI.11–12.7
SL.11–12.4

Write Proposal Decide which group members will be responsible for writing each part of the proposal. Using the chart above as a guide, begin by explaining what the title and main idea of your exhibit will be. Then summarize the aspects of chivalry you will focus on, the important points you want to make about these aspects (including how they relate to the excerpt from *A Distant Mirror*), and which media you will use to support your points. Explain how the information in your exhibit will be organized.

After all the content is written, peer review each other's work and make sure it all flows together logically and supports the main idea you want to convey. Follow the citation guidelines on pages R35–R37 of your textbook to cite your sources.

Present Your Proposal If you are not going on to Part 2 of the 21st Century Skills Project, your teacher may ask you to present your proposal as the end result of the project. You may also be evaluated on the presentation.

Name______________________ Class____________ Date____________

Display your proposal in a written or typed format that is visually appealing and presents the information clearly. Include sample print-outs of the media you describe in your proposal. Once your group is satisfied that the content is presented effectively, turn it in to your teacher.

PART 2 Create a Multimedia Exhibit

SL.11–12.5 After you've finished Part 1 of this project, create your multimedia exhibit based on your proposal. With your group, decide how you will present your exhibit. Will you show everything in a slide show format? Or will some information be conveyed on handouts or in another manner?

Make sure the information in your exhibit is visually appealing, clearly presented, and flows together logically. Be sure to make strategic use of digital media to enhance understanding of your findings. If you are using a slide show format, do not overload each slide with too much text. Make sure that images are interwoven with the text in a way that makes sense.

Rehearse your presentation in front of friends or family members before presenting to your class. Make sure that each person in your group knows which portions of the presentation he or she is responsible for. As you rehearse, make sure the transitions between presenters are smooth.

After you've completed this project, answer the following questions.

1. How well does your exhibit convey your main idea about chivalry?

____

____

____

____

2. Does your exhibit help support the author's main ideas in the excerpt from *A Distant Mirror* or does the exhibit present a different or opposing view? Explain.

____

____

____

____

Name ______________________ Class ____________ Date ____________

3. Does your exhibit flow well? Is information presented clearly? Explain.

____

____

____

____

4. What would you change in the planning, creation, and presentation of this project if you were to do it again?

____

____

____

____

Evaluate As you read and view your classmates' work, take notes about the content and effectiveness of their multimedia exhibits. Then use your notes to participate in a class discussion about the project.

1. Does the main idea about chivalry make sense? Is it adequately supported? Explain.

____

____

____

____

2. Does the exhibit take into account the ideas and arguments of the author in *A Distant Mirror*? Explain.

____

____

____

____

Name______________________ Class__________ Date__________

3. Is the information in the exhibit presented clearly and effectively? Explain.

4. What would you add or change in the exhibit? Why? Consider content and organization.

21st Century Skills Project

Name_________________________ Class_____________ Date_____________

Meditation 17

John Donne

Glencoe Literature, pages 430–434

RI.11–12.10

Before starting the lesson, read the following selections and complete the lesson activities in ***Glencoe Literature.***

"Meditation 17" **(pages 430–434)**

In this lesson you will analyze and discuss a reflective and deeply personal essay by the 17th-century poet, essayist, and homilist John Donne. You will then create a video version of Donne's prose meditation. Through your participation in the discussion and your work on the project, you will practice the following standards:

RI.11–12.2

Key Ideas and Details

- Determine two or more central ideas of a text and analyze their development over the course of the text, including how they interact and build on one another to produce a complex analysis.
- Provide an objective summary of the text.

RI.11–12.4
RI.11–12.6

Craft and Structure

- Determine the meaning of words and phrases as they are used in a text; including figurative, connotative, and technical meanings; analyze how the author uses and refines the meaning of a key term or terms over the course of a text.
- Determine an author's point of view or purpose in a text in which the rhetoric is particularly effective, analyzing how style and content contribute to the power, persuasiveness, or beauty of the text.

Group Discussion

Discussing nonfiction within a small group can help you grow as a reader and as a member of a learning community. Together, you and other group members can arrive at a better understanding of a selection, its ideas and craft, and its connection to other works and areas of study.

Name________________________ Class____________ Date____________

PLAN

RI.11–12.1
W.11–12.9, a
W.11–12.10
L.11–12.2, b

To prepare for discussion, build your content knowledge by examining the selection in greater detail. On your own, write your answers to the questions that follow, using text evidence. You may also write additional questions about the selection that you wish to discuss with your group. Your teacher may review your answers before the discussion, so be sure to use correct grammar, spelling, punctuation, and capitalization.

RI.11–12.4

Figurative Language Donne uses figures of speech to communicate abstract ideas. Two figures of speech that he uses are metaphor and metonymy.

- In a **metaphor,** one thing is equated with a seemingly unlike thing, for example, "Love is a boat without oars." The dissimilarity forces the reader to reach for connections that may not be obvious and, in the process, makes the first thing more clear and vivid.
- In an **extended metaphor,** several elements of one thing are equated with several elements of another; for example, "Love is a boat without oars on a raging river approaching a waterfall."
- A **metonymy** is a figure of speech that substitutes a word or phrase for something closely associated with it. For example, "Downing Street," where the prime minister lives in London, is often used to refer to the executive branch of the British Government

Group Discussion

In your own words, explain the following figures of speech used by Donne in his essay. Identify the type of figure being used, what it compares, and how the comparison helps you understand Donne's meaning. Cite additional text evidence as needed.

1. "all mankind is of one author and is one volume" (*British Literature*, page 431)

____

____

____

____

____

Name_______________ Class_______ Date_______

2. "never send to know for whom the bell tolls; it tolls for thee" (*British Literature,* page 432)

3. "No man is an island" (*British Literature,* page 432)

4. "affliction is a treasure" (*British Literature,* page 432)

5. How does Donne develop the metaphorical meaning of the term "affliction" in the last paragraph of his essay?

Group Discussion

Name ______________________ Class ____________ Date ____________

RI.11–12.6 In calling his reflective essay a "meditation," Donne invites the reader to imagine it as somewhat like listening in on a person's thoughts as he or she ponders something important and personal. **Voice** is the distinctive use of language that conveys the author's personality to the reader. Voice is determined by elements of style such as word choice and tone.

6. How would you describe the author's voice in this essay? Support your responses with specific examples of Donne's style, word choice, and tone.

Element of Voice	Text Example	Description of Voice
Style		
Word Choice		
Tone		

7. How does the voice of the essay reveal and support its purpose?

____

____

____

____

____

Group Discussion

Name ______________________ Class ______________ Date ______________

8. How do the style and content of the essay contribute to its power, persuasiveness, and beauty? Explain.

RI.11–12.2

A **theme** or **central idea** of an essay is a main point or message the author wants to convey to the reader. In a complex essay, there may be more than one theme or central idea.

9. Identify two themes or central ideas in "Meditation 17." How do these ideas develop, interact, and build on one another to produce a complex account of the human condition? Write your responses to these questions in the form of an objective summary of the text.

Group Discussion

Name________________ Class________ Date________

ASSIGN

SL.11–12.1, a

Meet with your literature group to plan your discussion. Each group member should become the expert on one or two of the questions answered on pages 90–93. Each expert will then guide the discussion on his or her question(s). List each group member and his or her question(s) in the chart below.

Group Member	Question(s) to Present

To become an expert on your question(s), spend some extra time thinking about your questions and consulting the text for relevant details. Building on your question(s), write down one or two discussion points or related questions for group members to consider as they explore text issues.

____

____

____

____

____

____

Group Discussion

Name________________________ Class____________ Date____________

DISCUSS

SL.11–12.1 a–d
SL.11–12.4
L.11–12.1
L.11–12.3

Break into your assigned literature group to conduct your discussion. The expert for question 1 should begin by reading aloud the question and leading the discussion in response. Follow this process for each question until you have covered them all.

Remember that literature groups contain room for disagreement. Healthy debate can help all members push their understanding to a new level. Use your time wisely so that you are able to discuss all the questions sufficiently.

In your discussion, follow the guidelines below.

Discussion Guidelines
▪ Come to discussions prepared; be sure you have carefully and thoroughly answered all questions. ▪ Express your ideas clearly. When presenting on your question and commenting on others, support your ideas with concrete evidence from the text. Give specific page numbers. ▪ Work with your group to promote civil, democratic discussions and decision making. ▪ Work with your group to set clear goals and deadlines. ▪ Establish individual roles as needed (i.e., note taker, moderator, etc.). ▪ Propel conversations by posing and responding to questions that probe reasoning and evidence. ▪ Ensure a hearing for a full range of positions on a topic or issue; clarify, verify, or challenge ideas and conclusions; and promote divergent and creative perspectives. ▪ Respond thoughtfully to diverse perspectives and synthesize comments, claims, and evidence made on all sides of an issue. ▪ Resolve contradictions when possible and determine what additional information or research is required to deepen the investigation or complete the task.

At the end of your discussion, be prepared to share the insights you have gained with your class. On the lines below, briefly summarize the most interesting ideas or insights you heard or experienced during the discussion.

____

____

____

____

____

____

Group Discussion

Name________________________ Class______________ Date______________

Meditation 17

John Donne

21st Century Skills Project **Music Video**

Now that you have analyzed and discussed the essay in detail, you will have the opportunity to extend your thinking about it creatively by participating in a group project. Your assignment is to create a music video version of Donne's meditation. In carrying out this project, you will follow the steps below:

- Select images, music, and other elements to include in your video.
- Create a storyboard to show what visual and sound elements you want to include and the order you want to present them in.
- If resources allow, shoot your music video and present it to your classmates and teacher.

Background Like works of literature generally, films fall into different genres. Most of the movies you are familiar with are narratives. They tell stories, whether fictional or true, and so they follow the rules of storytelling, which emphasize action and sequence. Other films, like documentaries or infomercials, have as their main purpose to convey information. Such films follow the rules of informational text, which emphasize facts, reasoning, and organization.

Music videos and other related films reproduce many of the characteristics of lyric poetry in cinematic form. Following is a list of techniques that are often used. You may think of others to add to the list. Refer to this list as you plan and create your music video.

- Images in a lyrical film are often metaphorical, symbolic, or intended to evoke a mood rather than to depict objects and events literally.
- Lyrical film is edited in a way that is nonlinear rather than sequential. The relationship between shots is often associative rather than logical. Images and scenes can be repeated like a refrain.
- While narrative and informational films rely heavily on synchronous sound—sound that is related realistically to what is shown (for example, the sound of traffic during a street scene), lyrical film relies more heavily on non-synchronous sound—sound that is dubbed over the visual track (such as theme music).

Name________________________ Class______________ Date______________

PART 1 Plan Your Music Video and Create a Storyboard

SL.11–12.1 b–d

With a small group, plan your music video. Use your plan to create a storyboard.

Most music videos are created to present a single piece of music, usually a song. Your music video should focus on the presentation of John Donne's reflective essay, "Meditation 17." You should not limit yourself to a single piece of music, because your video would inevitably become a presentation of the music. Instead, use a variety of musical and other sound elements in conjunction with images to capture the spirit of Donne's meditation as you see it.

W.11–12.9

Select Elements Meet with your group to generate ideas for visual and sound elements to include in your video. Answer the following questions to help you plan.

1. Which of Donne's images do you want to include in your video? How can you best render each image in a video format? Write your responses in the chart below.

Image from Text	Visual Presentation	Sound Presentation

21st Century Skills Project

Name____________________ Class____________ Date____________

2. Which of Donne's figures of speech do you want to include in your video? How can you best render this figure of speech in a video format? Write your responses in the chart below.

Figure of Speech	Visual Presentation	Sound Presentation

3. Filmmakers often use music or other sound elements to create a mood or convey feelings. You can also do this visually. For example, an image of a cast-off toy can suggest the poignancy of lost childhood innocence. Think about which elements of Donne's tone and emotions you want to convey and how. Record your ideas in the chart below.

Feeling and Tone	Visual Presentation	Sound Presentation

Name ______________________ Class ____________ Date ____________

Organize Elements Think about how you will organize your images and sounds to create a coherent whole. Answer the following questions to help you plan.

4. What will be your strategy for editing and ordering shots in your video? Will you include transitional or repeated images? How will the organization of your video support your take on Donne's style and theme?

____

____

____

____

____

____

Gather Content Gather the media elements you will need for your video. These might include the following, but you may want to add items of your own to the list.

- Videotaped footage of objects, people, or scenes
- Photographs
- Fine art such as paintings or statues
- Sketches, illustrations, or graphics that you create yourself
- Visual representations of text, such as a suggestive word or phrase
- Sound recordings, including musical passages
- Other: ______________________
- Other: ______________________

Decide which members of your group will be responsible for gathering which elements and create a list of assignments.

Name: ____________ Assignment: ____________

Name: ____________ Assignment: ____________

Name: ____________ Assignment: ____________

Name: ____________ Assignment: ____________

Name: ____________ Assignment: ____________

Name: ____________ Assignment: ____________

Name________________________________ Class______________ Date______________

Create a Storyboard Filmmakers use a storyboard to plan out each shot in a movie. Each individual camera shot is sketched out in small boxes in the storyboard to represent the sequence of shots. This allows everyone to know what the director wants each shot to look like and how shots should be ordered and connected.

With your group, create a storyboard frame for each shot in your video. Use information from your notes and graphic organizers to help you. You'll need to provide a sketch of each shot, as well as notes on shot composition, editing between shots, and any music or sound effects you want included. Be sure to key your story board to your outline and to include media file names for easy reference. Use the diagram below as a model.

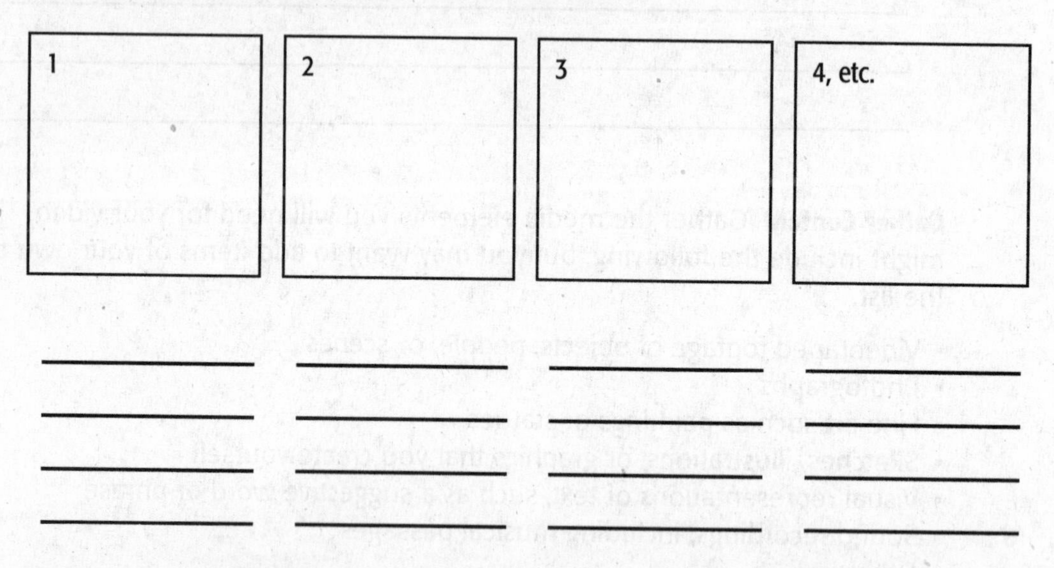

Present Your Storyboard If you are not going on to Part 2 of this 21st Century Skills project, your teacher may ask you to present your storyboard as the concluding activity of the project. You may also be evaluated on the presentation.

In presenting your storyboard you should provide a running commentary that explains each frame and makes a smooth transition between frames. To enhance the impact of your presentation, you can also show actual images or graphics along with individual frames, play sound recordings, or read aloud any text elements.

Once you have presented your storyboard, your teacher may ask you to turn it in, along with any images, graphics, or recordings you have assembled.

Name__________ Class__________ Date__________

PART 2 Film a Music Video

W.11–12.9

After your group has finished Part 1 of this project, use your storyboard to create your music video interpretation of Donne's meditation. With your group, answer the questions below to help plan the production.

1. What additional video footage and sound elements will we need to record?

2. What location(s) or studio resources will we need to record our video?

3. What recording equipment will we need? How will we get it?

4. What equipment will we need for music and other sound elements?

21st Century Skills Project

Name________________________ Class____________ Date____________

5. What type of video editing software will we use?

____

____

____

____

6. List the members of your group and the tasks each person will complete. Some tasks will need the help of more than one person.

Name: ______________ Task: ______________________

Name: ______________ Task: ______________________

Name: ______________ Task: ______________________

Name: ______________ Task: ______________________

Name: ______________ Task: ______________________

Name: ______________ Task: ______________________

Present Your Music Video After you've filmed and edited your video, review it for content, creativity, group work, and communication of ideas. If you have time, make changes to your video to strengthen any areas that seem weak. Then present it to the class.

After you've shown your music video to your class, answer the following questions with your group:

1. What worked well in your music video and why?

____

____

____

____

2. What would you change in the planning, creation, and presentation of this video if you were to do this project again?

____

____

____

____

21st Century Skills Project

Name______________________ Class__________ Date__________

SL.11-12.1
SL.11-12.2
SL.11-12.3

Observe and Evaluate As you view your classmates' videos, take notes about the films' success in presenting Donne's meditation, the creativity of their adaptations, and their overall aesthetic impact. Then use your notes to participate in a class discussion about the videos.

1. What approach does the video take to adapting Donne's text for the film medium?

____

____

____

____

2. How appropriate is this approach? In what ways is it creative and original?

____

____

____

____

3. How effectively does the video execute its plan and achieve its goals?

____

____

____

____

4. Apart from Donne's essay, what is the aesthetic impact of the video?

____

____

____

____

Name__________________ Class__________ Date__________

5. What would you add to or change in the music video? Why?

____

____

____

____

Name ____________________ Class __________ Date __________

A Modest Proposal

Jonathan Swift

Glencoe Literature: British Literature, pages 549–558

RI.11–12.10

Before starting the lesson, read the following selections and complete the lesson activities in ***Glencoe Literature: British Literature.***

"A Modest Proposal" **(pages 549–558)**

In this lesson you will analyze and discuss an excerpt from Jonathan Swift's well-known satire the "A Modest Proposal." You will then write your own satire and create your own blog to publish your satire as a blog post. Through your participation in the discussion and your work on the project, you will practice the following standards:

RI.11–12.4
RI.11–12.6

Craft and Structure

- Determine the meaning of words and phrases as they are used in the text, including figurative, connotative, and technical meanings.
- Determine an author's point of view or purpose in a text in which the rhetoric is particularly effective.

Group Discussion

Group Discussion

Discussing literature within a small group can help you grow as a reader and as a member of a learning community. Together, you and other group members can arrive at a better understanding of a selection, its ideas and craft, and its connection to other works and areas of study.

PLAN

RI.11–12.1
W.11–12.9, b
W.11–12.10
L.11–12.1
L.11–12.2, b

To prepare for discussion, build your content knowledge by examining the selection in greater detail. On your own, write your answers to the questions that follow, using text evidence. You may also write additional questions about the selection that you wish to discuss with your group. Your teacher may review your answers before the discussion, so be sure to use correct grammar, spelling, punctuation, and capitalization.

Name__________________ Class__________ Date__________

RL.11–12.6 **Point of View** As you learned from the lesson activities for this selection in *Glencoe Literature*, "A Modest Proposal" is a **satire**—a literary work that uses irony, humor, and other techniques to criticize problems and the people who are causing them. Swift takes the rhetorical device of irony a step further in this essay by creating a fictional speaker whose entire **point of view**—his way of looking at the world—and **tone**—his implicit attitude toward his subject and his audience—must be understood ironically. Through the rhetoric of irony, Swift's own point of view can be inferred as exactly the opposite of that of his fictional speaker.

1. How does the the fictional speaker view himself in this essay? How do you know? How does he view his proposal and his purpose in writing? Write your responses in the graphic organizer below. Support your responses with text evidence, including page references.

a. How the speaker views himself:
b. How the speaker views his proposal:
c. How the speaker views his purpose in writing:

2. How would you summarize the point of view of the fictional speaker in this essay?

____

____

____

____

____

____

Group Discussion

Name______________________ Class____________ Date____________

RI.11–12.4 **Tone and Word Choice** Swift gives his fictional speaker a **tone**—that is, an implied attitude toward the subject matter—appropriate to the speaker's point of view. One way Swift establishes tone is through the skillful use of diction, or word choice; specifically, through figurative language, word connotations, and technical language related to economics and cookery.

3. What examples of figures of speech, connotation, and technical language can you find in this essay? How do these word choices help establish the fictional speaker's tone and point of view? Write your responses in the graphic organizer that follows.

Word Choice	Speaker's Tone and Point of View
Figures of Speech	
Word Connotations	
Technical Language	

Group Discussion

Name________________________ Class____________ Date____________

4. Looking at the fictional speaker's point of view and tone through the lens of irony, how would you describe the author's point of view in this essay? Refer again to the examples you provided above for text evidence for your responses.

____

____

____

____

____

____

____

____

5. Where can you see the author stepping out of the mask of his fictional speaker and speaking from his own point of view in the essay? Explain your responses and support them with text evidence.

____

____

____

____

____

____

Name______________________ Class__________ Date__________

ASSIGN

SL.11–12.1, a, b

Meet with your literature group to plan your discussion. Each group member should become the expert on one of the questions on pages 106–108. Each expert will then guide the discussion on his or her question. List each group member and his or her question in the chart below.

Group Member	Question(s) to Present

To become an expert on your question, spend some extra time thinking about it and consulting the text for relevant details. Building on your question, write down one or two discussion points or related questions for group members to consider as they explore text issues.

____

____

____

____

____

Group Discussion

Name ______________________ Class __________ Date __________

DISCUSS

SL.11–12.1 a, c, d
SL.11–12.3
SL.11–12.4
L.11–12.1
L.11–12.3

Break into your assigned literature group to conduct your discussion. The expert for question 1 should begin by reading aloud the question and leading the discussion in response. Follow this process for each question until you have covered them all.

Remember that literature groups contain room for disagreement. Healthy debate can help all members push their understanding to a new level. Use your time wisely so that you are able to discuss all the questions sufficiently.

In your discussion, follow the guidelines below.

Discussion Guidelines
• Come to discussions prepared; be sure you have carefully and thoroughly answered all questions. • Express your ideas clearly. When presenting on your question and commenting on others, support your ideas with concrete evidence from the text. Give specific page numbers. • Work with your group to promote civil, democratic discussions and decision making. • Work with your group to set clear goals and deadlines. • Establish individual roles as needed (i.e., note taker, moderator, etc.). • Propel conversations by posing and responding to questions that probe reasoning and evidence. • Ensure a hearing for a full range of positions on a topic or issue; clarify, verify, or challenge ideas and conclusions; and promote divergent and creative perspectives. • Respond thoughtfully to diverse perspectives and synthesize comments, claims, and evidence made on all sides of an issue. • Resolve contradictions when possible and determine what additional information or research is required to deepen the investigation or complete the task.

At the end of your discussion, be prepared to share the insights you have gained with your class. On the lines below, briefly summarize the most interesting ideas or insights you heard or experienced during the discussion.

____

____

____

____

____

____

Group Discussion

Name______________________ Class____________ Date______________

A Modest Proposal

Jonathan Swift

21st Century Skills Project Satirical Blog

Now that you have analyzed and discussed Swift's "A Modest Proposal" in detail, you will have the opportunity to extend your thinking about it creatively by completing a group project. Your assignment is to write a satirical essay. If resources allow, you will create a blog and post your essay online. In carrying out this project, you will follow the steps below:

- Plan and Write a Satirical Essay
- Create a Blog
- Post Your Essay to the Blog

PART 1 Write a Satirical Essay

W.11–12.4

Write a satirical essay in which you present a critique of a political, social, or educational issue indirectly through an ironic point of view and tone. Be careful to avoid ridiculing particular individuals or groups of people by name or in a way that might be perceived as hateful or offensive.

If you create a blog and post your essay to it later, your fellow students will be able to post their comments on your essay and on the topic of your critique, and you in turn will be able to respond to their posts. Keep this in mind as you write.

With your group discuss the following questions to choose a topic for your essay and to develop your ideas before you begin writing. During or after your discussion, record your group's ideas and comments so that you can refer to them as you draft.

1. What are some situations, policies, activities, or social institutions that I think need might be worthy objects of satire? Generate several examples. Test your topic ideas by considering the following:
   - What is unreasonable, annoying, or unfair about this topic? Why does it need to be held up to the light of thoughtful criticism?
   - Can I satirize or reveal the absurdities of this topic through satirical techniques such as irony, exaggeration, understatement, or sarcasm?
   - Does this topic present opportunities for satirical humor?
   - Is this topic broad enough and significant enough to generate interest among my audience? Will they care?
   - Is this topic limited and specific enough to generate interest among my audience? Will it hold their interest?

Name____________________ Class____________ Date____________

- Does this topic have the potential to provoke a variety of thoughtful critical or satirical responses on a blog?

Record your ideas and conclusions in the chart that follows.

Idea for Satire	Evaluation of Idea

2. What will the fictional speaker in my essay be like? How will I reveal this character's point of view through his or her statements, assumptions, word choice, and tone?

____

____

____

____

3. What will my fictional speaker's proposal be about? How will it supposedly "solve" the problem it addresses?

____

____

____

____

Name________________________________ Class______________ Date______________

4. What will be the major ideas, components, or steps in my proposal?

____

____

____

____

____

____

5. How will I clue my reader in to the satirical elements of my essay so that my real point of view and purpose show through clearly?

____

____

____

____

Draft As you write your essay, keep the following tips in mind:

- Begin by establishing the nature of the problem you are writing about and your fictional speaker's motives and purpose in writing.
- Present your proposal in a clear thesis statement. Then present your main ideas or suggestions in a logical sequence with smooth transitions between them.
- Use tone, word connotations, figures of speech, and other aspects of diction such as level of formality to help establish the character of your fictional speaker and to help the reader see your speaker in a satirical light.
- Write a conclusion that sums up your ideas and reinforces your true point of view and purpose without stepping out of your satirical character.
- Give your essay an appropriately satirical title.

Use a separate page to create an outline and to record any additional notes for your satirical essay.

Name________________________ Class____________ Date____________

Present Your Essay If you are not going on to Part 2 of this 21st Century Skills Project, your teacher may ask you to present your essay orally or in writing as the end result of the project. You may also be evaluated on the presentation.

Before you present your essay to the class, practice reading it aloud on your own and in front of family members or friends. Don't rush your reading. Use your punctuation and line breaks to help you determine when to pause. Speak clearly and look at your audience. Vary your intonation to get your meaning across and to emphasize certain words or ideas. After you have presented your essay, your teacher may ask you to turn it in, along with any notes, graphic organizers, or drafts you have assembled.

PART 2 Create a Blog and Blog Post

SL.11–12.5

After you've finished Part 1 of this project, create a blog and post your satirical essay online. Your blog's interactive format will allow your fellow students to comment on your proposal and on the issue it concerns.

A **blog**, short for "web log," is an on-line journal created by one or more "bloggers." Bloggers write entries, or **posts**, on one or a variety of topics. A blog post may also include pictures, audio, and video.

A blog has a "comments" section for readers' opinions. The blogger may also allow readers to submit guest posts, which the blogger enters onto the blog. In this way, the blog allows users to discuss topics and share opinions.

Find a Blogging Platform Search online for a no-fee blogging service.
Register for an Account and Create Your Blog The blogging service will include a blog builder. Using an online service means you do not need to install blog software on your computer. Log in, then choose a design and add your content. Your blog will be your own Web site for sharing your ideas, thoughts and opinions on the topic of your satire.

Select Your Domain and Theme Complete the registration for your blog account. Make your blog your own by customizing your preferences.

Refine Your Design Decide if you would like to include images, music, other sounds, or video in your blog. Create these elements yourself. Taking these elements off of the Internet can be an infringement of copyright laws.

Name____________________ Class__________ Date__________

Add Hyperlinks If you decide that you need to include hyperlinks to images or other Web pages, you'll need to determine where these links should appear. Use these links to provide key background information on the issue that your story satirizes. Use the chart below to compile this information.

Links Needed	Location of Links in Content

21st Century Skills Project

Name______________________________________ **Class**________________ **Date**________________

W.11–12.6 **Publish and Present** After you've set up your blog and your teacher has approved, publish your satire as a post. To publish your post, hit a "publish" button, and the post becomes public on the Internet. Then email the URL to your teacher and classmates, who can read your work online and post their own responses on your blog. You may then want to respond to their comments and posts.

After you've completed this project, answer the following questions.

1. How does your blog and your blog post add to the presentation of your satirical essay?

2. How does the blog allow for dialogue and further exploration of your topic?

21st Century Skills Project

Name________________________ Class______________ Date______________

3. What would you change in the planning, creation, and presentation of this project if you were to do it again?

___

___

___

___

SL.11–12.1
SL.11–12.2
SL.11–12.3

Evaluate Go to your classmates' blogs and read the posts of their satirical stories. As you read and view your classmates' work, take notes about the content and effectiveness of their stories and their blog. Then use your notes to participate in a class discussion about the project.

1. Is the theme and central issue of each blog conveyed clearly? How well does each essay satirize the issue it is about? Explain.

___

___

___

___

2. Which supporting information and hyperlinks are most effective? Explain.

___

___

___

___

3. In what ways do music, other sounds, images, and video add to or take away from the effectiveness of each blog post?

___

___

___

___

Name________________ Class__________ Date__________

4. What would you add or change in the story or the blog? Why?

____

____

____

____

21st Century Skills Project

Name________________________ Class____________ Date____________

from The Introduction to Frankenstein

Mary Shelley

Glencoe Literature: British Literature, pages 792–798

RI.11–12.10 Before starting the lesson, read the following selections and complete the lesson activities in ***Glencoe Literature: British Literature.***

from "The Introduction to *Frankenstein*" **(pages 792–798)**

In this lesson you will analyze and discuss an excerpt from Mary Shelley's introduction to her famous novel. You will then create a documentary about the novel, its social significance, and the many ways it has had an impact on later books, movies, and genre fiction. Through your participation in the discussion and your work on the project, you will practice the following standards:

RI.11–12.1
RI.11–12.3

Key Ideas and Details

- Cite strong and thorough textual evidence to support analysis of what the text says explicitly as well as inferences drawn from the text, including determining where the text leaves matters uncertain.
- Analyze a complex set of ideas or sequence of events and explain how specific individuals, ideas, or events interact and develop over the course of the text.

RI.11–12.4
RI.11–12.5

Craft and Structure

- Determine the meaning of words and phrases as they are used in the text, including figurative, connotative, and technical meanings.
- Analyze and evaluate the effectiveness of the structure an author uses in his or her exposition or argument, including whether the structure makes points clear, convincing, and engaging.

RI.11–12.7

Integration of Knowledge and Ideas

- Integrate and evaluate multiple sources of information presented in different media or formats as well as in words in order to address a question or solve a problem.

Group Discussion

Discussing nonfiction within a small group can help you grow as a reader and as a member of a learning community. Together, you and other group members can arrive at a better understanding of a selection, its ideas and craft, and its connection to other works and areas of study.

Name________________ Class__________ Date__________

PLAN

RI.11–12.1
W.11–12.9, b
W.11–12.10
L.11–12.1
L.11–12.2, b

To prepare for discussion, build your content knowledge by examining the selection in greater detail. On your own, write your answers to the questions that follow, using text evidence. You may also write additional questions about the selection that you wish to discuss with your group. Your teacher may review your answers before the discussion, so be sure to use correct grammar, spelling, punctuation, and capitalization.

RI.11–12.3

Sequence of Events In her introduction, Shelly describes the sequence of events that led to her idea for the novel *Frankenstein*.

1. In the graphic organizer below, number and list in order the major events in the sequence.

1.	
2.	
3.	
4.	
5.	
6.	
7.	
8.	
9.	
10.	

Group Discussion

Name ______________________ Class __________ Date __________

2. Basing your answer on this sequence of events, how would you summarize Shelley's explanation of how she got the idea for the novel?

RI.11–12.1
RI.11–12.5

Structure and Interpretation Shelley might have organized her introduction by stating her idea for her novel and then listing reasons to support it. Instead she focuses on the steps that led to the discovery of her idea.

3. Why do you think Shelley decides to structure her introduction in this way? Are her points more clear, convincing, and engaging as a result of this structure or less so? Explain your responses.

4. Determine at least one important aspect of her explanation that Shelley leaves uncertain by taking this approach. How does this uncertainty affect your interpretation of the essay? Cite evidence for your response.

RI.11–12.4

Key Terms Shelley uses the term *hideous* five times in the excerpt. *Hideous* is an adjective that has two basic meanings:

a. Ugly or disgusting

b. Morally repugnant or despicable

Group Discussion

Name_____________________ Class__________ Date__________

5. In the graphic organizer below, examine each of the five uses of the term. Identify the word or concept it modifies. Then describe the context in which it is used.

Use	Modifies	Context
"so very hideous an idea" (page 793)		
"the hideous phantasm of a man" (page 797)		
"hideous corpse" (page 797)		
"hideous phantom" (page 797)		
"hideous progeny" (page 797)		

Group Discussion

6. How does Shelley's use of the term *hideous* change from the beginning of the excerpt to the end?

____

____

____

____

7. Why do you think Shelley compares her own creation, the novel *Frankenstein*, to the monstrous creation of her character Victor Frankenstein?

____

____

____

____

Name_________________________ Class_____________ Date_____________

ASSIGN

SL.11–12.1, a, b

Meet with your literature group to plan your discussion. Each member should become the expert for one or more of the questions on pages 120–122. Each expert will then guide the discussion on his or her question(s). List each group member and his or her question(s) in the chart below.

Group Member	Question(s) to Present

To become an expert on your question(s), spend some extra time thinking about your question(s) and consulting the text for relevant details. Building on your question(s), write down one or two discussion points or related questions for group members to consider as they explore text issues.

____

____

____

____

____

____

Group Discussion

Name________________________________ Class______________ Date______________

DISCUSS

SL.11–12.1 a, c, d
SL.11–12.3
SL.11–12.4
L.11–12.1
L.11–12.3

Break into your assigned literature group to conduct your discussion. The expert for question 1 should begin by reading aloud the question and leading the discussion in response. Follow this process for each question until you have covered them all.

Remember that literature groups contain room for disagreement. Healthy debate can help all members push their understanding to a new level. Use your time wisely so that you are able to discuss all the questions sufficiently.

In your discussion, follow the guidelines below.

Discussion Guidelines

- Come to discussions prepared; be sure you have carefully and thoroughly answered all questions.
- Express your ideas clearly. When presenting on your question and commenting on others, support your ideas with concrete evidence from the text. Give specific page numbers.
- Work with your group to promote civil, democratic discussions and decision making.
- Work with your group to set clear goals and deadlines.
- Establish individual roles as needed (i.e., note taker, moderator, etc.).
- Propel conversations by posing and responding to questions that probe reasoning and evidence.
- Ensure a hearing for a full range of positions on a topic or issue; clarify, verify, or challenge ideas and conclusions; and promote divergent and creative perspectives.
- Respond thoughtfully to diverse perspectives and synthesize comments, claims, and evidence made on all sides of an issue.
- Resolve contradictions when possible and determine what additional information or research is required to deepen the investigation or complete the task.

At the end of your discussion, be prepared to share the insights you have gained with your class. On the lines below, briefly summarize the most interesting ideas or insights you heard or experienced during the discussion.

____

____

____

____

____

____

Group Discussion

Name________________________ Class____________ Date______________

from The Introduction to Frankenstein

Mary Shelley

21st Century Skills Project **Documentary**

Now that you have analyzed and discussed the excerpt from the Introduction to *Frankenstein*, you will have the opportunity to extend your thinking about it creatively by participating in a group project. Your assignment is to prepare a film documenting the influence of the novel on literature and popular culture in the two centuries that have followed its first publication. In carrying out this project, you will follow the steps below:

- Do research to learn more about the impact of Shelley's novel.
- Create a storyboard to show what information you want to include, how you will present it visually, and how you will handle other aspects of the film such as voiceover narration and music.
- If resources allow, shoot your documentary film and present it to your classmates and teacher.

Background Mary Shelley's novel has had an enormous impact on literature and popular culture. A variety of film versions of her story exist, the best known of which is probably *Frankenstein* (1931), starring Boris Karloff. There have also been numerous B-movies and sequels based on the premise of a mad scientist who creates or reanimates a living person, for example, *The Bride of Frankenstein* (1935), starring Karloff and Elsa Lancaster. Among these are the well-known comedy *Young Frankenstein* (1974), starring Gene Wilder. In the Boris Karloff incarnation, the Frankenstein monster has taken on a life of its own as a cultural icon and is a figure that many children would recognize from cartoons and toys. The 1960s sitcom *The Munsters* featured a Frankenstein-monster character as the father. *Frankenstein* can probably also take some of the credit for the popularity of movies in the 1960s and 70s about zombies, for example, *Night of the Living Dead* (1968).

Many of these spin-offs hardly do justice to Shelley's work, but it is clear that she created a story that has continued to stir the imaginations of audiences for almost two centuries. Shelley must also be regarded as one of the earliest creators of the genre of science fiction. In fact, Shelley's introduction is, among other things, an account of how she became bored with the assignment of writing a "ghost story"—a story of pure fantasy—and found her inspiration instead in the moral and philosophical implications of hard science.

Name________________ Class____________ Date____________

PART 1 Conduct Research and Create Storyboards

With a small group, conduct research into the influence of Shelley's novel. Using the information you gather, create a storyboard for a documentary focusing on some aspect of the impact of Shelley's novel on later literature and popular culture.

W.11–12.5 **Limit Your Topic** The influence of Shelley's novel on literature and popular culture is a very broad topic. To be interesting and meaningful, your documentary will need to have a more specific focus, one that makes clear the thesis you are defending and why it matters. You may want to meet with your group at least twice to discuss the focus of your documentary: once before you begin research and again after you have done some basic research to determine whether your topic is a viable one or decide if you should modify your original plan to incorporate new ideas that you have discovered. Use the graphic organizer that follows to record your thinking and discussion.

Ideas for Limiting Your Topic	Related Initial Research Findings
1.	
2.	
3.	

New or Revised Topic	Related New Research Questions

21st Century Skills Project

Name ______________________ Class ______________ Date ______________

RI.11–12.7
W.11–12.7

Conduct Research Using print and online resources, locate information related to your topic. Be creative in your selection of sources. For example, you may find it useful to do images searches, consult movie databases, or to bring in statistical information in the form of charts or diagrams related to the history of the story's film versions, spin-offs, or success at the box-office. Use the graphic organizers that follow to record your findings. Make additional copies of this page as needed.

_____ Source # _____ Print _____ Digital _____ Text _____ Image _____ Footage _____ Graphic

Source digital file name (if applicable): ______________________

Description of Content:

Relevance to Thesis:

Source:

_____ Source # _____ Print _____ Digital _____ Text _____ Image _____ Footage _____ Graphic

Source digital file name (if applicable): ______________________

Description of Content:

Relevance to Thesis:

Source:

_____ Source # _____ Print _____ Digital _____ Text _____ Image _____ Footage _____ Graphic

Source digital file name (if applicable): ______________________

Description of Content:

Relevance to Thesis:

Source:

21st Century Skills Project

Name ______________________ Class ____________ Date ____________

Create a Storyboard Filmmakers use a storyboard to plan out each shot in a movie. Each individual camera shot is sketched out in small boxes in the storyboard to represent the sequence of shots in a scene. This allows everyone to know what the director wants each scene and shot to look like.

With your group, discuss what you want to include in your documentary about Frankenstein. Keep in mind that a documentary is a film that aims to document something real. Documentaries often include narration, interviews with experts, images, quantitative information, and footage of artifacts or materials related to the subject.

After you've discussed how you want to organize and present your documentary, create a storyboard frame for each shot in the film. Use information from your notes and graphic organizers to help you. You'll need to provide a sketch of how you want each shot to look, as well as notes on any voiceover narration, music, or sound effects you want included. Use the diagram below as a model.

1	2	3	4
______	______	______	______
______	______	______	______
______	______	______	______
______	______	______	______

5	6	7	8, etc.
______	______	______	______
______	______	______	______
______	______	______	______
______	______	______	______

21st Century Skills Project

Name ______________________ Class ____________ Date ____________

Answer the following questions to help guide you as you create your storyboard.

1. What title will we give our documentary to indicate its main idea and purpose?

   Title: ______________________________

2. How should we compose each shot? What do we want the audience to see?

3. What graphic imagery, such as movie stills or posters, do we wish to include?

4. What historical reenactments or narration should we include, if any?

5. What kinds of quantitative information do we want to include as support? How will we represent this information—through narration, charts, diagrams, or in some other way?

21st Century Skills Project

Name______________________ Class____________ Date____________

6. What camera angles, distance, and movement would best convey each sequence of shots? Do we need close-ups? Special visual effects?

____

____

____

____

7. How will we show divisions between different sections of the documentary? How will the shots in each section be connected through editing to create a coherent sequence?

____

____

____

____

8. What kind of sound do we want in each section? Voiceover narration? Background sounds? Special sound effects? Dramatic music?

____

____

____

____

Present Your Storyboard If you are not going on to Part 2 of this 21st Century Skills project, your teacher may ask you to present your storyboard as the concluding activity of the project. You may also be evaluated on the presentation.

SL.11–12.5 **Make Strategic Use of Digital Media** In presenting your storyboard you should provide a running commentary that explains each frame and makes a smooth transition between frames. If you have written narrative script as part of your preparation, you may want to incorporate it. To enhance the impact of your presentation, you can also read narrative script, show actual images along with individual frames, display graphics, play sound recordings, or read key passages from interview transcripts.

Once you have presented your storyboard, your teacher may ask you to turn it in, along with any images, scripts, or recordings you have assembled.

Name ____________________ Class __________ Date __________

PART 2 Film a Documentary

After your group has finished Part 1 of this project, use your storyboard to film a documentary about the influence of *Frankenstein*. With your group, answer the questions below to help plan the filming of your movie.

1. What location(s) will we use to film our documentary? Why?

2. If we're including reenactments, what scenery, props, and costumes will we need? Who will perform in the reenactments?

3. What equipment will we need for music and sound effects?

4. What camera, lighting, and film techniques will be most effective? Why?

Name______________________ Class____________ Date____________

5. What type of video editing software will we use?

6. List the members of your group and the tasks each person will complete. Some tasks will need the help of more than one person.

Name **Tasks**

Present Your Documentary After you've filmed and edited your documentary, review it for its content, creativity, group work, and communication of ideas. If you have time, make changes to your documentary to strengthen any areas that seem weak. Then present it to the class.

After you've shown your documentary to your class, answer the following questions with your group:

1. What worked well in your documentary and why?

Name________________________ Class____________ Date____________

2. What would you change in the planning, creation, and presentation of this documentary if you were to do this project again?

____

____

____

____

SL.11–12.1, a–d
SL.11–12.2

Observe and Evaluate As you view your classmates' documentaries, take notes about the content and effectiveness of their films. Then use your notes to participate in a class discussion about the documentaries.

1. What main idea is presented in the film?

____

____

____

____

2. Which supporting information and images are most effective?

____

____

____

____

3. How do the camera and editing techniques affect the tone of the film?

____

____

____

____

Name________________ Class________ Date________

4. What would you add to or change in the documentary? Why?

Name ________________________ Class ____________ Date ____________

from A Room of One's Own

Virginia Woolf

Glencoe Literature: British Literature, pages 1104–1110

RI.11–12.10

Before starting the lesson, read the following selections and complete the lesson activities in ***Glencoe Literature: British Literature.***

from *A Room of One's Own* **(pages 1104–1110)**

In this lesson you will analyze and discuss an excerpt from Virginia Woolf's *A Room of One's Own*. You will then write your own original audio podcast script dramatizing a social problem. You may also publish your audio podcast on an appropriate Web site. Through your participation in the discussion and your work on the project, you will practice the following standards:

RI.11–12.3

Key Ideas and Details

- Analyze a complex set of ideas or sequence of events and explain how specific individuals, ideas, or events interact and develop over the course of the text.

RI.11–12.4
RI.11–12.6

Craft and Structure

- Determine the meaning of words and phrases as they are used in a text, including figurative, connotative, and technical meanings.
- Determine an author's point of view or purpose in a text in which the rhetoric is particularly effective, analyzing how style and content contribute to the power, persuasiveness, or beauty of the text.

Group Discussion

Discussing literature within a small group can help you grow as a reader and as a member of a learning community. Together, you and other group members can arrive at a better understanding of a selection, its ideas and craft, and its connection to other works and areas of study.

PLAN

RI.11–12.1
W.11–12.9, b
W.11–12.10
L.11–12.1
L.11–12.2, b

To prepare for discussion, build your content knowledge by examining the selection in greater detail. On your own, write your answers to the questions that follow using text evidence. You may also write additional questions about the selection that you wish to discuss with your group. Your teacher may review your answers before the discussion, so be sure to use correct grammar, spelling, punctuation, and capitalization.

Name ______________________ Class __________ Date __________

RI.11–12.6 **Point of View and Rhetoric** In her essay Woolf supports her arguments with effective **rhetoric,** the art of using language persuasively. **Rhetorical devices** are techniques writers use to manipulate language for effect or to evoke an emotional response in the reader. Two rhetorical devices used by Woolf are **verbal irony** (using words to mean the opposite of what is stated directly) and **sarcasm** (using bitter or caustic language, often ironic, to point out shortcomings or flaws).

1. In the first paragraph of the excerpt (page 1105), how does Woolf use irony and sarcasm to contrast her approach to the topic with that of the "old gentleman"? How does this rhetorical strategy support her argument?

____

____

____

____

____

____

2. In paragraph two (pages 1105–1106), what reason does Woolf give for inviting the reader to imagine with her that Shakespeare had a sister? How effective is the rhetorical strategy of dramatizing what would happen to this sister if she had a gift for writing plays? Give reasons for your response.

____

____

____

____

____

____

____

____

____

Group Discussion

Name________________________ Class______________ Date______________

RI.11–12.3 **Complex Ideas and Events** In her story about the fate of Shakespeare's imaginary sister, Judith, Woolf describes a complex series of events in which multiple ideas are interwoven.

3. Using the graphic organizer that follows, identify the main events in the sequence Woolf imagines taking place in Judith's life.

1.

↓

2.

↓

3.

↓

4.

↓

5.

↓

6.

↓

7.

Group Discussion

Name_________________________________ Class______________ Date______________

4. According to Woolf on page 1107, what three possibilities await the woman who is born with Shakespeare's gift? Why are these the only choices?

____

____

____

____

5. According to Woolf on page 1107, even if a woman succeeds in producing literary works, what else can happen to prevent her from becoming recognized as a genius?

____

____

____

____

Group Discussion

Name______________________ Class__________ Date__________

RI.11–12.4 **Connotative and Figurative Meanings** In telling Judith's story, Woolf supports her purpose with **connotations,** the suggested or implied meanings associated with words or phrases beyond their dictionary definitions, and with **figures of speech,** expressions that are not literally true but express some truth beyond the literal level.

6. In column 1 of the graphic organizer that follows, read the words or phrases from Judith's story (pages 1106–1107). Then, in columns 2 and 3, identify the relevant connotations of the italicized words or phrases and explain how they support Woolf's purpose.

Word or Phrase	Connotation	Support for Purpose
mind the stew		
moon about with books and papers		
scribbled		
not to *hurt* him, not to *shame* him		
guffawed, bellowed		
took pity, gentleman		

Group Discussion

Name________________________ Class______________ Date__________

7. Identify two figures of speech in the sentence that follows and explain how they support Woolf's purpose in describing Judith's fate.

Yet her genius was for fiction and lusted to feed abundantly on the lives of men and women and the study of their ways. (page 1106)

8. Basing your answer on your responses to the previous questions, summarize Woolf's ideas about why "it would have been impossible…for any woman to have written the plays of Shakespeare in the age of Shakespeare."

Group Discussion

Name ______________________ Class ____________ Date ____________

ASSIGN

RI.11–12.5
SL.11–12.1, a, b, d

Meet with your literature group to plan your discussion. Each group member should become the expert on one or more of the questions on pages 136–140. Each expert will then guide the discussion on his or her question(s). List each member and his or her question(s) in the chart below.

Group Member	Question(s) to Present

To become an expert on your question(s), spend some extra time thinking about your question(s) and consulting the text for relevant details. Building on your question(s), write down one or two discussion points or related questions for group members to consider as they explore text issues.

____

____

____

____

____

____

Group Discussion

Name____________________ Class__________ Date__________

DISCUSS

SL.11–12.1 a–d

Break into your assigned literature group to conduct your discussion. The expert for question 1 should begin by reading aloud the question and leading the discussion in response. Follow this process for each question until you have covered them all.

Remember that literature groups contain room for disagreement. Healthy debate can help all members push their understanding to a new level. Use your time wisely so that you are able to discuss all the questions sufficiently.

In your discussion, follow the guidelines below.

Discussion Guidelines
• Come to discussions prepared; be sure you have carefully and thoroughly answered all questions. • Express your ideas clearly. When presenting on your question and commenting on others, support your ideas with concrete evidence from the text. Give specific page numbers. • Work with your group to promote civil, democratic discussions and decision making. • Work with your group to set clear goals and deadlines. • Establish individual roles as needed (i.e., note taker, moderator, etc.). • Propel conversations by posing and responding to questions that probe reasoning and evidence. • Ensure a hearing for a full range of positions on a topic or issue; clarify, verify, or challenge ideas and conclusions; and promote divergent and creative perspectives. • Respond thoughtfully to diverse perspectives and synthesize comments, claims, and evidence made on all sides of an issue. • Resolve contradictions when possible and determine what additional information or research is required to deepen the investigation or complete the task.

At the end of your discussion, be prepared to share the insights you have gained with your class. On the lines below, briefly summarize the most interesting ideas or insights you heard or experienced during the discussion.

____

____

____

____

____

____

Group Discussion

Name______________________________ Class______________ Date______________

from A Room of One's Own

Virginia Woolf

21st Century Skills Project **Podcast**

Now that you have analyzed and discussed the essay in detail, you will have the opportunity to extend your thinking about it creatively by participating in a group project. Your assignment is to write an audio podcast that presents an argument in narrative or dramatic form. In carrying out this project, you will follow the steps below:

- Choose a topic about which you can write argumentatively.
- If necessary, research this topic to get specific information you need.
- Write a narrative or dramatic script to present your argument.
- If resources allow, post an audio file of a performance of your script to a Web page or blog.

Background In the story of Judith, Woolf presents a nonfictional argument in the form of a fictional narrative. Doing so allows her to use the resources of the imagination to present her thoughts with a lot of vivid clarity and colorful detail.

PART 1 Write a Podcast

W.11–12.3 a–e

With a small group, write an audio podcast that presents an argument in narrative or dramatic form. Before you begin writing, use the following questions and strategies to help guide you.

21st Century Skills Project

Name ______________________ Class ____________ Date ____________

SL.11–12.1, b, d
SL.11–12.4

Brainstorm Ideas With a small group, brainstorm appropriate controversial questions or issues about which you care and would like to express an opinion. Take notes on the lines below.

After you have brainstormed ideas, choose one issue that your group wants to write about. Describe the issue on the line below.

What aspects of this issue lend themselves to presentation in the form of a story? (Hint: It is easier to dramatize the view you disagree with, as Woolf does.)

Name _______________ Class _______ Date _______

W.11–12.5 **Outline Your Story** Create an outline for your story. Use the graphic organizer that follows to record your ideas.

TITLE:	
Main character(s): **Other characters:**	**Setting:**
Conflict:	**Complications and Resolution:**
Mood, Tone, Irony:	
Theme(s):	

Decide on a Script Format You should write your script in the format you want it to be in when your audience listens to it. You have three options:

- Tell your story entirely through narration and indirect quotation (as does Woolf).
- Include dialogue in the form of direct quotations that could be read by other members of your group.
- Write your story in dramatic form, that is, entirely in dialogue, with stage directions for any additional sound elements you want to include.

However you format your script, include notes to the reader(s) about emphasis, pauses, pace, volume, tone, and other elements that will enhance the impact of your podcast.

21st Century Skills Project

Name ______________________ Class ____________ Date ____________

Create Your Script Once you have decided how you want to format your story, you can create your audio podcast script. You may want to write out every word of the script and perform it word for word. Or you may want to prepare notes that your narrator and other readers can refer to and plan to record your podcast as an improvisation. Decide which members of your group will be responsible for individual writing or performing tasks:

Member:	**Task:**
Member:	**Task:**
Member:	**Task:**
Member:	**Task:**
Member:	**Task:**
Member:	**Task:**

Edit Because you may have to turn in your script as part of the assignment, be sure to create a clean, well-formatted copy. Correct any errors in grammar, usage, mechanics, and spelling. Consult your textbook's Language Handbook on pages R40–R59 and use your computer's grammar and spelling check features as needed.

Present Your Story If you are not going on to Part 2 of the 21st Century Skills Project, your teacher may ask you to present your podcast orally as the end result of the project. You may also be evaluated on the presentation.

Before you present your podcast to the class, practice performing it aloud on your own and in front of an audience. Use your script notes to help you deliver your lines effectively. Speak clearly and look at your audience. After you have presented your podcast orally, your teacher may ask you to turn in your script, along with any notes, graphic organizers, or drafts you have assembled.

Name____________________ Class__________ Date__________

PART 2 Record and Publish an Audio Podcast

After you've finished Part 1 of this project, record your script and publish it online as a podcast. A **podcast** is a digital audio or video file available on the Internet for people to listen to and/or watch. For this assignment, you will create an audio podcast. To begin planning your recording session, answer the questions below.

1. What sound recording equipment will we need? Where will we get it?

2. Will we record first onto a storage device such as a CD and then upload the file or record directly onto a computer? What type of audio file will we create and what software will we need for it?

3. Is the software already installed on the computer? If not, where will we find it? Will we need additional software to edit the file?

4. Where will we record our podcast? Why is it a good location for a sound recording?

21st Century Skills Project

Name ______________________ Class ____________ Date ____________

5. Where will we publish the audio podcast? Will our class post its podcasts on our school or class Web site or will we need to create individual Web pages or blogs?

____

____

____

____

Record Your Podcast Before you begin recording, check all equipment to be sure it is functioning properly. Record your podcast. If someone makes a mistake, don't worry about it during recording. You can edit it out later.

Edit Your Audio File Now begin the editing stage. First edit out any parts of your recording that you don't want in your podcast. Then add any introductory, transitional, or concluding material, such as the title of your podcast and any sources or contributors you wish to credit. Save the edited audio file on your computer or on a removable storage device.

W.11–12.6

Create Your Podcast Once your teacher has approved your podcast, upload the file to the Web site your class is using. If necessary, send the URL of the site to your teacher and classmates, so they can listen to your podcast .

After you've published your podcast, answer the following questions with your group.

1. What worked well in your podcast and why?

____

____

____

____

2. What would you change in the planning, creation, and presentation of this podcast if you were to do this project again?

____

____

____

____

Name_______________ Class_______________ Date_______________

SL.11–12.1
SL.11–12.2
SL.11–12.3

Observe and Evaluate As you listen to your classmates' podcasts, take notes about the content and effectiveness of their dramatizations. Then use your notes to participate in a class discussion about the films.

1. What argument is the dramatization presented in the podcast intended to convey?

____

____

____

____

2. How effectively does the dramatization convey the intended argument? Explain.

____

____

____

____

3. How effectively was the dramatization performed? Explain.

____

____

____

____

4. What is your evaluation of the quality of the sound recording and digitalization? What other aspects of the podcast delivery technology did you find helpful or problematic? Explain.

____

____

____

____

Name__________ Class__________ Date__________

5. What would you add or change in the podcast? Why?

Writing Workshops

Name ______________________ Class ____________ Date ____________

Writing Workshop

PERSUASIVE ESSAY

Glencoe Literature Connection: from *A Vindication of the Rights of Woman*, pages 696–703

Before starting the lesson, read the following selections and complete the lesson activities in ***Glencoe Literature: British Literature.***

A Vindication of the Rights of Women, by Mary Wollstonecraft **(pages 696–703)**

In this lesson, you will study an excerpt from Mary Wollstonecraft's essay *A Vindication of the Rights of Women*. You will analyze how the author effectively uses the argumentative writing methods and techniques listed below. You will then write your own argument using these methods and techniques. As you complete this workshop, you will practice the following standards:

W.11–12.1, a, b

Develop Claims and Counterclaims

- Introduce precise, knowledgeable claims and establish their significance.
- Distinguish claims from alternate or opposing claims.
- Create an organization that logically sequences claims, counterclaims, reasons, and evidence.
- Develop claims and counterclaims fairly and thoroughly.
- Provide evidence for claims and counterclaims while pointing out the strengths and limitations of both in a way that anticipates the audience's knowledge level, concerns, values, and possible biases.

W.11–12.1, c

Use Transitions

- Use words, phrases, clauses, and varied syntax to link sections of text.
- Use transitional language to create cohesion and clarify the relationships between claims and reasons, between reasons and evidence, and between claims and counterclaims.

W.11–12.1, d

Use Appropriate Style and Tone

- Establish and maintain a formal style and objective tone.
- Attend to the norms and conventions of the discipline in which you are writing.

W.11–12.1, e

Provide a Conclusion

- Write a concluding statement or section that follows from and supports the argument presented.

Name ______________________ Class ____________ Date ____________

Analyze and Prewrite

Develop Claims and Counterclaims

Persuasion is writing that attempts to convince readers to think or act in a certain way. An **argument** is a type of persuasive writing in which logic and reason are used to try to influence a reader's thoughts or actions. In an argument, a statement about a problem or an issue is called a **claim**.

Support for a claim can include logical reasoning and evidence, such as examples, facts, and expert testimony. In addition, to make their arguments stronger, writers often anticipate and respond to opposing claims with **counterclaims**—statements that argue against opposing claims and support the original claim.

LEARN FROM THE MODEL

Reread the first paragraph of the excerpt (page 697) to explore how Wollstonecraft presents her initial claims.

1. What main claim(s) does the author introduce in this paragraph? How does she establish the significance of the claim(s)?

____

____

____

____

____

____

2. How does Wollstonecraft show that her claim is knowledgeable and precise? How does she distinguish it from alternate or opposing claims?

____

____

____

____

____

____

Argument

Name ______________________ Class ____________ Date ____________

3. How does Wollstonecraft organize her claims into a logical sequence? Fill in the following graphic organizer showing the chain of cause-and-effect that she describes. Then write your summary of how she has organized her claims on the lines that follow the organizer.

Claim:

↓

Claim:

↓

Claim:

↓

Claim:

↓

Claim:

↓

Claim:

____

____

____

____

Name______________________ Class______________ Date______________

4. How does Wollstonecraft anticipate her audience's

- Knowledge Level?
- Concerns?
- Values?
- Possible Biases?

Choose several key passages and write your responses in the graphic organizer that follows.

Passage	Implicit Claim	Anticipates Audience's...

Argument

Name________________________ Class______________ Date______________

W.11–12.1, a, b
W.11–12.5

APPLY WHAT YOU'VE LEARNED

5. Use the graphic organizer below to identify your essay's most important claims and counterclaims fairly and thoroughly. Make as many copies of this organizer as you need—one for each of your major claims.

My Precise Claim	Evidence for Claim
Strengths/Limitations of Claim	**Anticipates Audience's...** (knowledge, concerns, values, biases)
Known or Anticipated Opposing Claim	**Evidence for Opposing Claim**
Strengths/Limitations of Opposing Claim	**Anticipates Readers'...**
Counterclaim	**Evidence for Counterclaim**
Strengths/Limitations of Counterclaim	**Anticipates Readers'...**

Argument

Name______________________ Class______________ Date______________

6. Review your responses to question 5. Then, in the boxes below, develop the most important opposing claims you will need to address and explain in more detail how you will respond to them fairly and thoroughly. Make additional copies of this page as needed.

Opposing Claim: ______________________

____

____

Counterclaim: ______________________

____

____

Opposing Claim: ______________________

____

____

Counterclaim: ______________________

____

____

Opposing Claim: ______________________

____

____

Counterclaim: ______________________

____

____

Name____________________ Class__________ Date__________

7. Organize your claims, counterclaims, reasons, and evidence into a logical sequence. Put your organization into the form of an outline for your essay. Remember that an effective outline not only shows the sequence of ideas but also how they are grouped and related logically. Write your outline on the lines that follow or on a computer. Many word-processing programs offer an outline view option with automatic formatting.

Topic: ____________________

Use Transitions

In writing persuasively, it is important to use words, phrases, clauses, and varied syntax to link the major sections of the text, to create cohesion, and to clarify the relationships between claims and reasons, between reasons and evidence, and between claims and counterclaims.

Argument

Name____________________ Class__________ Date__________

LEARN FROM THE MODEL

1. Read the passages from the excerpt in column 1 of the chart below. In column 2, explain the transitional idea used in the passage. In column 3, explain the type of transitional language used. When you have completed rows 1–3, find three other transitional passages in the excerpt and complete rows for them. The first row has been completed as an example.

Passage	Transitional Idea(s)	Type(s) of Language
"After considering the historic page and viewing the living world with anxious solicitude, [I] confess that either nature has made a great difference between man and man or that...civilization...has been very partial." (page 697)	Emphasizes that she has come to her conclusions not hastily but only after studying history and observing society; says she wants to begin by honestly admitting that women are not equal to men.	Introductory adverb clause that varies syntax ("After... solicitude"), gerund phrases ("considering... page" and "viewing... world"), adjective paired with a noun ("anxious solicitude")
"One cause of this barren blooming I attribute to a false system of education..." (page 697)		
"...but as the subject lies in my way, and I cannot pass it over without subjecting... my reasoning to misconstruction, I shall stop a moment to deliver...my opinion." (page 698)		

Argument

Name______________________ Class__________ Date__________

W.11–12.1, c
W.11–12.5
L.11–12.3, a

APPLY WHAT YOU'VE LEARNED

2. Review your outline. Make a list of transitional ideas that you can use to create cohesion and clarify the relationships between claims and reasons, between reasons and evidence, and between claims and counterclaims. Indicate where on the outline you want to use the idea. Then consider possible words, phrases, clauses, and/or ways of varying syntax (word order) that you can use to convey these transitional ideas. Write your responses in the graphic organizer than follows.

Outline #	Transitional Idea	Transitional Language

Argument

Name______________________ Class__________ Date__________

Use Appropriate Style and Tone

In writing persuasively, it is important to establish and maintain a formal **style** and objective tone while attending to the **norms and conventions** of the discipline in which you are writing.

LEARN FROM THE MODEL

Style refers to the expressive qualities of a person's writing, including word choice, sentence structure, and the use of figurative language and imagery. Tone is an author's attitude toward his or her subject matter or audience as conveyed through content, word choice, figures of speech, and rhetorical devices.

1. How would you describe Wollstonecraft's style in the excerpt? Write your response in the graphic organizer that follows. Include three examples from the text and explain how they support your description.

Wollstonecraft's Style	Text Examples and Explanations

Argument

Name________________ Class__________ Date__________

2. How would you describe Wollstonecraft's tone in the excerpt? Write your response in the graphic organizer that follows. Include three examples from the text and explain how they support your description.

Wollstonecraft's Tone	Text Examples and Explanations

Norms and conventions refer to the use of language, methods, criteria, and style appropriate to a particular kind of writing. For example, in natural or social science, it is conventional to provide statistics and information about their validity. In a personal essay, it may be normal to use sarcasm or make jokes, but both would usually be inappropriate for a formal essay.

3. What norms and conventions does Wollstonecraft observe in the excerpt? Write your response in the graphic organizer that follows. Include three examples from the text.

Argument

Name________________ Class__________ Date__________

Norms and Conventions Observed	Text Examples

Argument

W.11–12.1d
W.11–12.5

APPLY WHAT YOU'VE LEARNED

4. Will your essay fall into a particular academic discipline (such as literary studies, social studies, or science) or will it be a more general type of persuasive writing such as that found in the op-ed section of a newspaper? Either way, what norms and conventions apply to the kind of writing you will do? What are some specific ways you can observe these norms and conventions?

5. What are some specific ways you will establish and maintain a formal style in your essay?

6. What are some specific ways you will establish and maintain an objective tone in your essay?

Argument

Provide a Conclusion

In writing persuasively, it is important to provide a concluding statement or section that follows from and supports the argument you have presented.

LEARN FROM THE MODEL

Read the last three paragraphs of the excerpt (page 701).

1. How do these paragraphs follow from and support the argument Wollstonecraft has presented?

Name____________________ Class__________ Date__________

2. How would you describe the strategy for concluding the argument that these paragraphs embody?

W.11–12.1, e
W.11–12.5

APPLY WHAT YOU'VE LEARNED

3. What will be your strategy for concluding your argumentative essay? How will your conclusion follow from and support the argument you have presented? How will your conclusion give your essay a sense of completeness and closure?

Argument

Draft

W.11–12.10

Before you begin drafting, review your prewriting notes on pages 154–166. Then write your first draft on a computer, following the instructions below.

Write the Introduction

W.11–12.1, d

Begin by writing the introductory paragraph or paragraphs of your persuasive essay. Your introduction should include

- a statement of your position on the issue and your basic reason for holding it
- a statement of what you want your reader to do in response
- an explanation of the context of your argument (or at least a reference to the context if you can assume your reader knows about it)
- an explanation of why your topic matters

Remember to establish a formal style and an objective tone in your introduction.

Name ______________________ Class __________ Date __________

W.11–12.1a, b, c, d

Write the Body

Use your outline to guide you as you write the body of your essay. Remember to support your claims with reasons and evidence. You will also need to distinguish your claims from alternate or opposing claims or counterclaims and include responses, or brief arguments against opposing opinions. One way to do this is to use transitional words, phrases or clauses to create cohesion, or clarity, between the different claims. You might wish to present claims, opposing claims, and counterclaims by using sentence frames like the following:

- "Opponents to this issue say that ________, but the evidence shows that ________."
- "Many will probably disagree with my assertion that ________, because ________, but ________."
- "Some of you may challenge my claim that ________. After all, many believe that ________. Indeed, my own claim that ________ seems to ignore ________. However, ________."

Be sure to develop your claims, counterclaims, and responses fairly by supplying evidence to support them. Point out the strengths and limitations of your claims and counterclaims based on your audience's knowledge level and concerns. Read the annotated model below to get an idea of how to present claims, opposing views, counterclaims, and evidence.

Claim: The starting time for our school should be changed from 7:00 A.M. to 8:00 A.M. to give students extra time for sleep.

Opposing View: Opponents of the later starting time have blamed students' sleep habits, rather than the school's schedule, for the fact that students are so sleepy. Several community members have argued that we should focus on teaching students to go to bed earlier.

Counterclaim and Evidence: While it is true that students need to be taught good sleep habits, studies have shown that teenagers actually remain more alert later at night than adults. In addition, they continue producing melatonin, the chemical responsible for sleepiness, far longer into the morning than adults.

Anticipation of Audience Concern: Changing the starting time for school would enable students to live healthier lives and do better academically, things we all care about.

Note that the writer anticipates possible concerns from the audience about the later starting time by acknowledging the validity of the opposing claim ("While it is true that students need to be taught good sleep habits"). The writer then presents a solid response that is supported by evidence. The writer proceeds to anticipate further audience concerns about students' health by stating that the later starting time would improve students' health.

Argument

Name______________________ Class__________ Date__________

As you write, make sure the organization of your speech establishes clear relationships among claims, counterclaims, reasons, and evidence. Maintain the formal style and objective tone that you established in the introduction.

Write the Conclusion

W.11–12.1, e

Finally, write the conclusion of your essay. Make sure it follows from and supports your argument. Your conclusion could be a single paragraph, or it could be several paragraphs, depending on what you want to do in it. Following are some things a well-written conclusion can do:

- restate your main claim forcefully or with an added twist
- summarize your strongest claims
- present a final synthesis of all your ideas
- connect persuasively with your audience
- suggest next steps, questions, or areas of exploration

Revise

W.11–12.4
W.11–12.5

To revise your essay, you will be focusing on the content, or the message, of your writing and possibly applying one or more of these four revision strategies:

- **add** details and information to make the message clearer
- **remove** distracting or unnecessary words or ideas
- **substitute** more precise or stronger words for bland or overused language
- **rearrange** phrases and sentences to be sure the message is logically presented

The questions that follow will show you how to use these revision strategies and help you consider how well the development, organization, and style of your essay are suited to task, purpose, and audience. Evaluate your essay and check each box when your essay meets the criteria.

Focus and Coherence

☐ Does my essay have a clear focus?

☐ Do all the parts work together so that I achieve my purpose?

Organization

W.11–12.1, a, e

☐ Does the beginning introduce my argument and its significance?

☐ Does the middle follow an organization that establishes clear relationships among claims, counterclaims, reasons and evidence?

☐ Does the conclusion follow from and support my argument?

Argument

Name______________________ Class__________ Date__________

W.11–12.1, a, b

Development of Ideas

☐ Did I introduce claims and distinguish them from alternate or opposing claims?

☐ Did I develop my claims and counterclaims fairly, supplying evidence for each?

☐ Did I present the strengths and limitations of my claims and counterclaims in a way that anticipates my audience's knowledge level and concerns?

W.11–12.1, d
L.11–12.3

Voice—Word Choice

☐ Is my choice of words persuasive?

☐ Did I establish and maintain a formal style and an objective tone?

☐ Did I apply knowledge of language to make effective choices for meaning or style?

W.11–12.1, c

Voice—Sentence Fluency

☐ Does my writing flow smoothly?

☐ Does my essay include transitional words, phrases, and clauses to link major sections of text?

☐ Did I use words, phrases, and clauses to clarify the relationships between claims, counterclaims, reasons, and evidence?

☐ Did I emphasize important points?

Edit and Proofread

Correct Errors in Grammar

L.11–12.3, a

Editing involves correcting errors in grammar, usage, mechanics, and spelling. As you edit, make sure your work conforms to the guidelines in a style manual that is appropriate for this type of writing. Check with your teacher to see which style guide you should use for reference.

Begin the editing stage by taking a careful look at your sentences. Make sure that each sentence expresses a complete thought in a way that is grammatically correct. Use the checklist below to edit your sentences.

SENTENCE-EDITING CHECKLIST

☐ Have I avoided sentence fragments?

☐ Have I avoided run-on sentences?

☐ Do verbs agree with their subjects?

☐ Are pronouns used correctly?

☐ Are verbs used correctly?

☐ Have I avoided misplaced and dangling modifiers?

Argument

☐ Have I used phrases and clauses correctly?

☐ Have I used parallel structure?

Correct Errors in Mechanics and Spelling

L.11–12.2, b

Next, check for and correct any errors in mechanics (punctuation and capitalization) and spelling.

Use the checklist below to edit your essay.

You should also use a dictionary to check and confirm spellings.

PROOFREADING CHECKLIST

☐ Are commas and other punctuation marks used as needed?

☐ Are all words spelled correctly?

☐ Are capital letters used as needed?

Present/Publish

W.11–12.6

After you have written and polished your essay, you will want to publish and present it. You may wish to consider some of these publishing and presenting options:

- Present your essay orally to your class.
- Use your essay as a springboard for a class debate.
- Publish a multimedia version of your essay online with accompanying links and images.

Consider using technology, including the Internet, to publish your essay, taking advantage of technology's capacity to display information flexibly and dynamically. You may wish to consult some of the projects in the Reading section of this book for additional publishing ideas that include technology.

Name________________________________ Class______________ Date______________

Grammar Practice: Usage

Usage

Usage refers to the way words and phrases are actually used in a language community. In speaking and writing, good or correct usage is generally considered to be that which speakers and writers traditionally have followed. Usage rules have been developed over time to regularize tradition, and people today are often expected to follow these rules, especially in formal speaking and writing situations.

English usage is often the subject of debate. Some experts may insist that something is wrong, while others insist that it is perfectly acceptable. Moreover, just as language itself changes over time, so do the rules of usage. When authoritative sources disagree about a particular usage, we say that the usage is **contested.**

The best reference tool for resolving issues of usage is a usage dictionary or other usage reference work. Even a good general dictionary will have usage information such as the following:

- **Usage labels** that indicate usage issues related to time, region, or style (such as *obsolete*, meaning the word is no longer used in this way; *British*, meaning the word is used this way in Britain; and *slang*, meaning the word is not appropriate for formal situations).
- **Illustrations of usage or usage notes** (for example: *grist* <that's grist for the mill>; *oyez* –used by a court official to gain attention)
- **Usage paragraphs** (placed with words that present problems of complex, confused, or contested usage) that give detailed information about a word's usage history, current usage, and different synonyms corresponding to different uses

Following are some good reference works on usage: *Merriam-Webster's Dictionary of English Usage,* H. W. Fowler's *A Dictionary of Modern English Usage,* and Theodore Bernstein's *Miss Thistlebottom's Hobgoblins.*

Argument

Name______________________________ Class______________ Date______________

L.11–12.1, 1a, 1b

Word Usage

Word usage refers to the sense in which words and phrases are used—the meaning they are intended to convey. Following are three common types of word-usage issues that may arise in your assigned speaking and writing.

- Substitution errors, that is, using one word for another that looks or sounds similar. There are many pairs of words in English that are commonly mistaken for one another, for example, *affect/effect*, *farther/further*, and *accept/except*. Correct usage in these situations can be determined simply by checking a word's definition or definitions in a good dictionary to make sure you have the right word.
- Using words in unconventional ways. For example, if you are playing ping-pong and you tell your partner to *pitch* the ball, you might be misunderstood or at least viewed as odd. Traditionally, you *pitch* the ball in baseball and *serve* the ball in ping-pong and tennis.
- Using words and phrases that are acceptable in some contexts and not in others. This problem generally arises when the words or phrases used are considered nonstandard, slang, regional dialect, jargon (specialized technical language), or argot (the language of a particular social group or situation, such as text messaging). Examples would be using the nonstandard word *ain't* in a formal debate, using the slang word *ginormous* in a formal essay, or using the abbreviation *LOL* for "laugh out loud" on an essay test.

Argument

Exercise A: Word Usage

Each of the of the underlined words or phrases in the sentences below raise a word-usage issue. Use a good standard dictionary with usage notes or a usage dictionary to check the usage. Then on the line below the sentence identify the type of usage issue raised and write a word or phrase that would solve the problem.

1. The economic situation had a powerful affect on the election.

____

2. The doctor told me to take two acetyl salicylic acid tablets and call her in the morning.

____

3. I'm going to graduate in May; leastways, I hope I am.

____

4. I decided to take the day off and just lay around the house.

____

5. What are you trying to infer by saying that I'm late "again"?

____

Name ______________________ Class __________ Date __________

L.11–12.1, a, b

Grammar Usage

There are some grammatical rules that should never be broken. There are many others for which it is true that, in breaking them, you risk being perceived as ignorant or careless of the rules. In most formal speaking and writing situations, therefore, following the traditional rules is likely to improve both the clarity and effectiveness of your communication.

However, like the rules of word usage, the rules of grammar usage generate disagreement among experts, and can change over time. In addition, some rules can be broken if you have a good reason for doing so.

Make a checkmark in the blank space preceding each of the rules below that you have ever encountered.

___**1.** A paragraph must always consist of more than one sentence.

___**2.** A singular subject always requires a singular verb, and a plural subject always requires a plural verb.

___**3.** An introductory clause must always be followed by a comma.

___**4.** Avoid very long, complicated sentences.

___**5.** Never begin a sentence with *And* or *But*.

___**6.** Never end a sentence with a preposition.

How many of these rules did you check? Many people have heard all of them, and all of them can be found in many lists of rules, but you may not have heard them. Nonetheless, it might surprise you to know that, of those listed, only rule number 3 is actually a hard-and-fast rule that should never be broken. The others are valid in some instances but often not in others.

Argument

Name________________________ Class______________ Date______________

Exercise B: Grammar Usage

Each of the following sentences or pairs of sentences breaks a traditional rule of grammar. For each sentence, identify the rule or rules that it breaks. Then explain why you think the grammar usage in the item is effective or ineffective.

6. What is that novel about?

7. Some people may agree with the ideas in an essay, some may disagree.

8. I read an essay that said that masculine women were criticized throughout society. But, the writer added, what does "masculine women" mean?

9. It was the best of times, it was the worst of times, it was the age of wisdom, it was the age of foolishness, it was the epoch of belief, it was the epoch of incredulity, it was the season of Light, it was the season of Darkness, it was the spring of hope, it was the winter of despair.

10. If, as the writer said, a woman's charms are "oblique sunbeams," it cannot have much effect on her husband.

Check Your Writing

Read through your argumentative essay to check for and correct any errors you may have made in usage. Use a standard or usage dictionary as needed.

Argument

Name______________________ Class__________ Date__________

Writing Workshop

RESEARCH REPORT

Glencoe Literature TIME: Death By Mosquito, pages 618–622

Before starting the lesson, read the following selection in ***Glencoe Literature: British Literature.***

"TIME: Death By Mosquito" **(pages 618–622)**

In this lesson, you will study the TIME article "Death By Mosquito" to discover how the author effectively uses the informative/explanatory writing and research methods and techniques listed below. You will then write your own research report using these methods and techniques. As you complete this workshop, you will practice the following standards:

W.11–12.7
W.11–12.8

Conduct Research

- Conduct research to answer a question or solve a problem, narrowing or broadening the inquiry when appropriate.
- Gather information from multiple authoritative print and digital sources.
- Assess the strengths and limitations of each source in terms of the task, purpose, and audience.
- Synthesize multiple sources.
- Integrate information into the text to maintain the flow of ideas.
- Avoid plagiarism and overreliance on any one source.
- Follow a standard format for citations.

W.11–12.2 a,b

Develop a Topic

- Introduce and develop a topic by selecting the most significant and relevant facts, extended definitions, concrete details, quotations, or other information and examples appropriate to the audience's knowledge of the topic.
- Organize complex ideas, concepts, and information so that each new element builds on that which precedes it to create a unified whole.
- Include formatting, graphics, and multimedia when useful to aiding comprehension.

W.11–12.2, c, d

Use Transitions and Precise Language

- Use appropriate and varied transitions and syntax to link the major sections of the text, create cohesion, and clarify the relationships among complex ideas and concepts.
- Use precise language, domain-specific vocabulary, and techniques such as metaphor, simile, and analogy to manage the complexity of the topic.

Informative Text

Name______________________ Class__________ Date__________

W.11–12.2, e

Establish and Maintain a Formal Style and Tone

- Establish and maintain a formal style and an objective tone.
- Use the norms and conventions of the discipline in which you are writing.

W.11–12.2, f

Provide a Conclusion

- Provide a conclusion that follows from and supports the information or explanation presented.

Analyze and Prewrite

Conduct Research

Informative/explanatory texts, or expository texts, examine and convey complex ideas, concepts and information. One type of informative/explanatory text that you are probably familiar with is a research report. This type of writing involves exploring a topic by conducting original research, evaluating the research of others, or a combination of both. The writer may also state an opinion on a topic and back it up with evidence found in outside sources.

Whatever the writer's assignment, purpose, or topic, the research process usually involves the following steps:

- Choose a topic by thinking about one's interests and choosing a topic that is important enough to generate interest, broad enough to allow serious research, and limited enough to investigate fully in the time and space available.
- Narrow or broaden a research topic based on the topic, task, purpose, and available resources on the topic.
- Generate a major research question that will be answered in the research report. For example, if someone were to write a report about the *Brown v. Board of Education* court case, a research question might be, "Why does this court decision matter?"
- Do preliminary research on the Internet for potential sources for the topic.
- Compile a list of online sites and print resources to investigate further.
- Look for evidence from experts and texts written for informed audiences in the field.
- Avoid overreliance on any one source.

You may choose or be assigned a research topic in a particular academic discipline such as literary studies, social studies, or science. If so, you will need to make sure that your report conforms to the norms and conventions of that discipline as well as to any additional guidelines specified by your teacher.

As writers conduct research on their topics, they gather relevant information from multiple authoritative sources and assess the usefulness of each source in answering the research question. Writers may need to broaden or narrow their inquiry as they proceed, based on information they discover.

Name________________________ Class____________ Date____________

LEARN FROM THE MODEL

Reread "Death By Mosquito" to determine what research methods the author may have used.

1. What is the topic of this report? What major research question might the author have used to help focus the report?

2. What discipline(s) is the topic of this article relevant to? What norms and conventions does the article adhere to?

3. Based on the in-text citations provided throughout the article, does it seem as though the author used multiple authoritative sources? How well did the writer synthesize the sources in the article? Explain.

Name________________ Class________ Date________

W.11–12.5

APPLY WHAT YOU'VE LEARNED

4. What topic will your research report be about? Remember that as you conduct research, you will narrow the topic or broaden it based on available resources on the topic and on any conflicting or significant information you find during your research.

5. What will your major research question be?

6. What authoritative print and online sources will you use to gather information? Conduct preliminary online research and then list at least six possible sources on the lines below. The sources should be a combination of digital and print sources.

Develop a Topic

Good writers of informative/explanatory texts choose to write about topics that are interesting and can be developed thoroughly by selecting the following:

- The most significant and relevant facts
- Extended definitions
- Concrete details
- Quotations
- Other information and examples appropriate to the audience's knowledge

Name_______________________________ Class_______________ Date_______________

Most writers of articles written for the general reader assume that their audience will need ample background and basic information. Whereas writers of scholarly articles for academics or advanced-level students would assume a certain knowledge base within their field of expertise and would build on that knowledge in their writing without including basic information.

LEARN FROM THE MODEL

Reexamine the body paragraphs of "Death By Mosquito" to see how the author develops the topic.

1. What information and examples does the author use to develop the topic throughout the report? Refer to the article and record examples of each type of research finding in the chart that follows.

Support Used to Develop Topic
Significant and Relevant Facts:
Extended Definitions:
Concrete Details:
Quotations
Other Information Appropriate to the Audience's Knowledge:

Informative Text

Name ______________________ Class __________ Date __________

2. What organizational structure does the author use to convey the ideas and information about malaria? Is this structure effective? Explain.

3. The author includes several images and graphics showing quantitative information in the article. Pick two and answer the following questions about them on the lines below. What purpose do these images and graphics serve? How do formatting elements (such as image captions, section headings, and the quotation pulled from the body of the text, enlarged, and boxed at the top of page 621) aid comprehension?

Informative Text

W.11–12.2, a, b
W.11–12.5

APPLY WHAT YOU'VE LEARNED

4. As you conduct research on your topic, take notes on note cards (see pages R31–R37 of your textbook for more help). Using your notes, create an outline to help you organize your complex ideas, concepts, and significant, relevant facts for your report. Include some of the facts, extended definitions, concrete details, quotations, or other information and examples that you will use to develop your topic.

Remember that an effective outline not only shows the sequence of ideas but also how they are grouped and related logically. Write your outline in the space provided on the following page or on a computer. Many word-processing programs offer an outline view option with automatic formatting and controls for rearranging ideas or changing their level in the outline. You can usually specify the outline type and format you wish to follow in your document.

Name____________________ Class__________ Date__________

Topic or Title: ____________________

5. What images (such as photos or drawings), graphics (such as charts, diagrams, or maps), formatting (such as heads and subheads), and multimedia elements (such as video clips) will you use in your report to help aid comprehension?

Informative Text

Name________________________________ Class______________ Date______________

Use Transitions and Varied Syntax

Good writers use transitions, such as words, phrases, and clauses, to link sections of text and create a cohesive, or organized report. Using varied, appropriate transitions helps clarify the relationships among complex ideas and concepts.

Good writers also vary their syntax, or the pattern that phrases or sentences form or create. Language or sentence grammatical patterns help support a type of writing, such as expository or research, emphasizing points and supporting the text's cohesion and relationships.

Transitions include words that show

- time order, such as *after, before, finally,* and *meanwhile*
- spatial relationships, such as *above, beyond, here,* and *within*
- importance or degree, such as *furthermore, in addition, above all,* and *most important*

Another transitional device is the repetition of key words or phrases or reference to ideas stated previously. For example, in "Death By Mosquito" the sentence that introduces the third paragraph uses both a transitional word (*however*) and one that presents a logical contrast (*hope*) with the previous two paragraphs:

> There is reason for hope, however. (page 618)

Variations in syntax often go hand-in-hand with transitions. Writers can use syntax to emphasize and link ideas and to clarify the relationship between an argument's claims, reasons, and evidence. Consider the sentence that introduces the first paragraph under the heading "Understanding the Disease:"

> To better understand why malaria has become such a threat and what can be done to stop the disease, it helps to know a little biology. (page 620)

In beginning this sentence with an infinitive phrase, the writer has placed a reference to the earlier part of the essay at a transition point. Anyone reading the sentence can know what has come before, what is coming next, and how the two sections are related.

Examples of varied syntax that writers use include

- starting a sentence with a descriptive word, with a phrase, or with a clause
- varying sentence length or alternating shorter sentences with longer ones
- varying sentence structure, such as simple, compound, and complex
- using parallelism, or pairs or a series of words, phrases, or sentences that have the same grammatical structure. The use of parallelism calls attention to the items in the series and creates unity in writing.

Name______________________ Class__________ Date__________

LEARN FROM THE MODEL

Reread "Death By Mosquito" and analyze how the author uses transitions and varies syntax.

1. Identify three examples of helpful transitions. Write the transition in the left column of the chart that follows. Then in the right column explain how the transition functions in the essay.

Transition	How It Functions

2. Identify three examples of transitional variations in syntax. Write the sentence containing the variation in the left column of the chart that follows. Then in the middle column explain how the syntax has been varied in the passage, and in the right column explain how the variation supports the transition.

Passage Containing Syntax Variation	How the Syntax is Varied in the Passage	How the Variation Supports the Transition

Name____________________ Class____________ Date____________

W.11–12.2, c, d, W.11–12.5 L.11–12.3, a

APPLY WHAT YOU'VE LEARNED

3. Review your outline on page 181. What words, phrases, or clauses would help make your transitions from point to point clear? Jot down several possible transitions below.

____

____

____

____

____

4. Pick one point from your outline and write a few sentences below using transitions to create cohesion and to link this point to another idea you want to discuss.

____

____

____

____

____

____

____

5. Review the explanations of syntax and your exploration of syntax on pages 182–183. What examples of syntax will you use in your writing to emphasize and link your ideas? In the first column of the chart that follows, write down several sentences in which you use examples of varied syntax for your report. In the second column, explain how your use of syntax will link sections of your text, create overall cohesion, or clarify relationships among the ideas and concepts you present.

Informative Text

Name_______________________________ Class_____________ Date_____________

Examples of My Use of Varied Syntax	Effect on My Text's Structure

Use Precise Language and Domain-Specific Vocabulary

Good writers also use precise and domain-specific language and techniques such as metaphor, simile, and analogy to manage the complexity of the topic they are writing about. Precise language includes detailed description and specific examples. An example of domain-specific vocabulary would be the use in a report on regrigeration of technical vocabulary specific to the topic such as *refrigerant, compressor,* and *condenser*.

One especially helpful use of precise language is **analogy,** or comparison of one thing to another that is similar but more familiar or easy to understand. Comparisons can also be made using **figurative language,** such as similes and metaphors. A **simile** is a figure of speech that uses like or as. A **metaphor** is a figure of speech that equates or compares two seemingly unlike things. Figurative comparisons can be powerful aids in conceptualizing difficult ideas and complexities.

Name________________ Class__________ Date__________

LEARN FROM THE MODEL

Analyze how the author of "Death By Mosquito" uses precise and domain-specific language and techniques such as metaphor, simile, and analogy to manage the complexity of the topic.

1. Identify three examples of precise language that relates to an academic and/or technical domain. How does this language help clarify the author's ideas?

Example of Precise Language	Academic or Technical Domain It Belongs To	How the Language Clarifies Ideas

2. Identify three examples of comparison (such as an analogy, a simile, or a metaphor) that the author of "Death By Mosquito" uses to clarify ideas.

Comparison	Type of Comparison	What It Clarifies

Name______________________ Class__________ Date__________

APPLY WHAT YOU'VE LEARNED

W.11–12.2, d
W.11–12.5

3. Review the outline that you created on pages 180–181 for your topic. What are some ideas that you can clarify using precise language such as detailed description or specific examples?

Idea: ______________________

Precise language: ______________________

____

Idea: ______________________

Precise language: ______________________

____

Idea: ______________________

Precise language: ______________________

____

4. What domain-specific language will you need to include in your report? Use the chart below to list six domain-specific words or expressions that you will use in your report. For each word or expression, identify the domain(s) it belongs to, and explain its meaning in everyday language.

Domain-Specific Language	Domain It Belongs To	What It Means

Name ______________________ Class ______________ Date ______________

5. Review your topic and outline and think about ideas and complexities that you could make clearer with techniques such as analogies and figurative comparisons (such as similes and metaphors).

Idea or complexity: ______________________

Precise language: ______________________

____

Idea or complexity: ______________________

Precise language: ______________________

____

Idea or complexity: ______________________

Precise language: ______________________

____

Establish and Maintain a Formal Style and Tone

In an informative or explanatory text, a writer should maintain a relatively formal style and an objective tone, or attitude, so that readers know the text is credible and unbiased. An important element of style is diction, or choice of words.

LEARN FROM THE MODEL

Reread passages from "Death By Mosquito" as indicated below and analyze how the author establishes and maintains a formal style and tone.

1. On page 618, what words and phrases contribute to a formal style? How? Find at least two examples. Use the chart below to address these questions.

Word or Phrase	How It Contributes to Formal Style

Informative Text

2. How would you describe the tone, or attitude, of the entire report? Support your response with evidence from the text.

____

____

____

____

____

W.11–12.2, e
W.11–12.5

APPLY WHAT YOU'VE LEARNED

As you write your report

- Use a formal vocabulary and avoid all slang words or expressions.
- Use correct grammar and syntax, consulting references for guidance as needed.
- Use diction, word connotations, and figures of speech to convey your tone.

3. Look at your outline on page 181 and choose one paragraph to develop on the lines below. Focus on establishing and maintaining a formal style and an objective tone as you write.

____

____

____

____

____

____

____

____

____

Provide a Conclusion

An effective conclusion in an informative or explanatory text should follow from and support the information or explanation that the writer has presented. Strong conclusions often reinforce the significance of the topic or tie the essay to larger ideas.

Informative Text

Name ____________________ Class ____________ Date ____________

LEARN FROM THE MODEL

Analyze how the author of "Death By Mosquito" constructs an effective conclusion.

1. What is the main idea in the last section of the article ("Stop Mosquitoes Before They Bite," page 621)? How does this idea connect to the rest of the article?

2. How does the last paragraph represent a conclusion to the main idea of the section and of the article as a whole? How does the last paragraph point beyond the article to a larger context?

W.11–12.2, f
W.11–12.5

APPLY WHAT YOU'VE LEARNED

3. Use the lines below to jot down possible ideas for the conclusion of your report. How will the conclusion relate to the rest of your report? What final thought might you leave with the reader?

Informative Text

Name ______________________ Class __________ Date __________

Draft

W.11–12.10

Before you begin drafting, review your prewriting notes on pages 176–190. Then write your first draft on a computer, following the instructions below.

Write the Introduction

W.11–12.2, a, e

Begin by writing the introductory paragraph or paragraphs of your research report. Your introduction should

- grab the reader's attention with something like an interesting anecdote, a surprising fact, or a thought-provoking question.
- introduce your topic.
- present your thesis statement, or controlling idea.
- establish a formal style and an objective tone.

Write the Body

W.11–12.2, a, b, c, d, e W.11–12.7 W.11–12.8

Write Cohesive Paragraphs Use your outline to guide you as you write the body of your report. Begin each paragraph with a topic sentence. Then develop your topic with well-chosen, relevant, and sufficient facts; extended definitions; concrete details; quotations; or other information and examples that are appropriate to your audience's knowledge of the topic. Organize ideas and information in a way that allows you to build on your ideas purposefully. Synthesize ideas and information from multiple sources into a coherent whole.

Use Transitions and Varied Syntax Use transitional words and expressions and varied syntax to link major sections of text and help you clarify the relationships between ideas.

Use Precise Language, Domain-Specific Language, and Literary Techniques Remember to use precise language and vocabulary that is specific to your topic.

Use Formatting and Graphics As you write, remember to include formatting when appropriate (such as heads and subheads) to help guide your readers. Consider including graphics (such as tables, maps, or graphs) and/or multimedia elements (such as links to video clips) if they will help readers comprehend your topic.

Credit Your Sources As you write, maintain the formal style and objective tone that you established in the introduction. Choose your words carefully to convey both the meaning and the tone that you want. Avoid plagiarizing, or presenting an author's words or ideas as if they are your own. You must credit your sources not only for material directly quoted but also for any facts or ideas obtained from the source. Follow a standard format for your citations and include a Works Cited list at the end of your report. See pages R31–R37 in your textbook for more information.

Name ______________________ Class ______________ Date ______________

Write the Conclusion

W.11–12.2, f

Finally, write the conclusion of your report. Make sure it follows from and supports the information or explanation you presented in your report. The conclusion should restate your thesis statement in a different way and summarize the main points in the report. You should try to end with a strong closing statement that leaves a lasting impression and articulates the significance of your topic.

Revise

W.11–12.4
W.11–12.5

To revise your research report, you will be focusing on the content, or the message, of your writing and possibly applying one or more of these four revision strategies:

- **add** details and information to make the message clearer
- **remove** distracting or unnecessary words or ideas
- **substitute** more precise or stronger words for bland or overused language
- **rearrange** phrases and sentences to be sure the message is logically presented

The questions that follow will show you how to use these revision strategies and help you consider how well the development, organization, and style of your report are appropriate to task, purpose, and audience. Evaluate your report and check each box when your report meets the criteria.

Focus and Coherence

☐ Does my report have a clear focus?

☐ Do all the parts work together so that I achieve my purpose?

Organization

W.11–12.2, a, f

☐ Does the beginning introduce my topic?

☐ Does the middle organize complex ideas, concepts, and information to make important connections and distinctions?

☐ Does the conclusion follow from and support the information or explanation I presented in the report?

Name ______________________ Class ______________ Date ______________

W.11–12.2, b

Development of Ideas

☐ Does my report reflect a logical progression of ideas?

☐ Did I develop the topic with well-chosen, relevant, and sufficient facts; extended definitions; concrete details; quotations; or other information and examples that are appropriate to my audience's knowledge of the topic?

W.11–12.2, d, e, L.11–12.3, a

Voice—Word Choice

☐ Did I use precise language, domain-specific vocabulary, and literary techniques?

☐ Did I apply knowledge of language to make effective choices for meaning or style?

☐ Did I establish and maintain a formal style and an objective tone?

☐ Did I use appropriate and varied transitions and syntax?

W.11–12.2, c

Voice—Sentence Fluency

☐ Does my writing flow smoothly?

☐ Does my report include various transitions to link major sections of text, create cohesion, and clarify the relationships among complex ideas and concepts?

☐ Did I emphasize important points?

Edit and Proofread

Correct Errors in Grammar

L.11–12.3, a

Editing involves correcting errors in grammar, usage, mechanics, and spelling. As you edit, make sure your work conforms to the guidelines in a style manual that is appropriate for this type of writing. Check with your teacher to see which style guide you should use for reference.

Begin the editing stage by taking a careful look at your sentences. Make sure that each sentence expresses a complete thought in a way that is grammatically correct. Use the checklist on the next page to edit your sentences.

Name____________________ Class__________ Date__________

SENTENCE-EDITING CHECKLIST

☐ Have I avoided sentence fragments?

☐ Have I avoided run-on sentences?

☐ Do verbs agree with their subjects?

☐ Are pronouns used correctly?

☐ Are verbs used correctly?

☐ Have I avoided misplaced and dangling modifiers?

☐ Have I used phrases and clauses correctly?

☐ Have I used parallel structure?

Correct Errors in Mechanics and Spelling

L.11–12.2, b

Next, check for and correct any errors in mechanics (punctuation and capitalization) and spelling.

Use the checklist below to edit your speech.

You should also use a dictionary to check and confirm spellings.

PROOFREADING CHECKLIST

☐ Are commas and other punctuation marks used as needed?

☐ Are all words spelled correctly?

☐ Are capital letters used as needed?

Informative Text

Present/Publish

W.11–12.6

After you have written and polished your research report, you will want to publish and present it. You may wish to consider some of these publishing and presenting options:

- Create a class anthology.
- Enter your report into a writing contest.
- Publish your report on the Internet.

Consider using technology, including the Internet, to publish your report, taking advantage of technology's capacity to display information flexibly and dynamically. You may wish to consult some of the projects in the Reading section of this book for additional publishing ideas that include technology.

Name ______________________ Class ____________ Date ____________

Grammar Practice

Syntax

Syntax is the broad term for principles that govern how words fit together to make sentences. Syntax is governed by structural elements and the parts of speech that make up each element.

For writing to be effective, its syntax must

- observe the conventions (or rules) of grammar, usage, and idiomatic language
- have enough variety to avoid seeming repetitive and monotonous
- express style, tone, or voice appropriate to a specific context

Structural Elements

L.11–12.3, a

Varying the types of sentences used in writing is key to holding readers' interest. There are four basic sentence structures: simple, compound, complex, and compound-complex. Incomplete sentences may be used in some types of writing for special effect.

For more information about the parts of a sentence and about sentence types, see *Glencoe Literature: British Literature,* "Language Handbook," pages R40–R46.

Exercise A: Recognizing Tone or Voice Conveyed By Syntax

These quotations from "At the Pitt-Rivers" convey the informal perspective and language of a teen-ager, but from time to time the speaker's tone is more serious and mature. On the line preceding each item, write **C** for casual or **S** for serious.

___**1.** It's a weird place, really weird, stuff from all over the world crammed into glass cases, like some kind of mad junk-shop.

___**2.** She still wasn't pretty, but she had the most beautiful expression I've ever seen in my life. She glowed: that's the only way I can put it.

___**3.** I got a bit fed up with the way some of my mates were sniggering about it, being all-knowing; truth to tell, I doubt if they know any more than I do, it's all just show.

___**4.** Looking at those two—watching them, if you like—was a bit like seeing something go on behind a thick glass window, so it was half removed from you.

___**5.** I was thinking about this—looking at a case of particularly loony stuff to do with witchcraft—when I saw them again.

Informative Text

Name ______ Class ______ Date ______

L.11–12.3, a

Parts of Speech and Their Functions

Below are the parts of speech that make up a typical sentence:

- Nouns and pronouns (such as *bloke* and *she*) name people or things.
- Verbs (such as *ignored* or *was*) express action or a state of being.
- Adjectives (such as *radiant* and *benign*) and adverbs (such as *clearly* and *well*) modify other parts of speech.
- Prepositions (such as *at* and *from*) and conjunctions (such *as and* or *but*) connect words, phrases, and clauses.

Words in English may shift from one part of speech to another. Its function in a sentence is what determines its part of speech. For example:

- *Ground* can be a noun but acts as an adjective in the phrase *ground floor.*
- *Even* can be an adjective but acts as an adverb in the phrase *even existed.*
- *Whatever* can be an adjective but acts as a pronoun in the clause *whatever I went there for.*

Exercise B: Recognizing Parts of Speech Based on Syntax

On the line before each item, identify the underlined words as a noun (**n**), an adjective (**adj**), an adverb (**adv**), or a preposition (**prep**), depending on how the word is used in its sentence. Refer as needed to ***Glencoe Literature: British Literature,*** "Language Handbook," pages R40–R46.

___**6.** One kind of <u>fossil</u> creature might be more evolved than another.

___**7.** Other times it looks to me <u>pretty</u> awful.

___**8.** I was busy with some <u>thinking</u> I wanted to do.

___**9.** And then they walked on, <u>round</u> the gallery again . . .

___**10.** I saw them go <u>past</u>—just their heads, above the glass cases..

L.11–12.3, a

Vary Syntax for Effect

In addition to making your writing more lively and interesting, varying your syntax can be a way of creating effects that make your writing clearer and more powerful. Following are some common effects than can be created by varying syntax:

- Emphasizing one part of a sentence by putting it first *Getting a college degree is exactly what I hope to accomplish by working hard.*
- Showing the relationship between two or more words or ideas in a sentence by how they are arranged *Dealing with friends' flattery can be as difficult as dealing with enemies' insults.*
- Creating parallel structures or antitheses *You're not experiencing a disaster; you're experiencing a growth opportunity.*

Informative Text

Name______________________________ Class______________ Date______________

- Creating a transition by connecting a sentence to previous material through an introductory phrase or clause *Although most of the efforts to combat crime I have mentioned so far have failed, there is one shining exception.*
- Connecting a sentence to other parts of your essay, including anticipating ideas that come later *Another reason for the collapse of the economy was the policy (the causes of which I will explain in the next chapter) of extending unsecured credit.*

Exercise C: Vary Syntax for Effect

Choose five sentences from your research report or from another essay that could be improved by varying the syntax. First write each sentence as it is now. Then write a new version in which you vary the syntax for effect. Finally, explain how you have changed the sentence and what effect you wanted to create.

11. ____

12. ____

Name Class Date

13.

14.

15.

Check Your Writing

Check your research report for the syntax you have used. Is your grammar correct? Do your words fit together gracefully? Are the tone and style in line with what you want them to be? Have you avoided needless repetition and choppiness? Make any changes you need to make to improve the syntax of your story.

Name ______ Class ______ Date ______

Writing Workshop

SHORT STORY

Glencoe Literature Connection: "At the Pitt-Rivers," pages 1193–1202

Before starting the lesson, read the following selections and complete the lesson activities in ***Glencoe Literature: British Literature.***

"At the Pitt-Rivers," by Penelope Lively **(pages 1193–1202)**

In this lesson, you will study Penelope Lively's short story "At the Pitt-Rivers" to discover how the author effectively uses the narrative writing methods and techniques listed below. You will then write your own short story using these methods and techniques. As you complete this workshop, you will practice the following standards:

W.11–12.3, a

Engage and Orient the Reader

- Set out a problem, situation, or observation and its significance.
- Establish one or multiple points of view.
- Introduce a narrator and/or characters.

W.11–12.3, a, c

Sequence Events

- Create a smooth progression of experiences or events.
- Sequence events so that they build on one another to create a coherent whole.

W.11–12.3, b, d

Use Narrative Techniques

- Use techniques such as dialogue, pacing, description, reflection, and multiple plot lines, to develop experiences, events, and/or characters.
- Use precise words and phrases, telling details, and sensory language to convey a vivid picture of the experiences, events, setting, and/or characters.

W.11–12.3, e

Provide a Conclusion

- Provide a conclusion that follows from and reflects on what is experienced, observed, or resolved over the course of the narrative.

Analyze and Prewrite

Engage and Orient the Reader

Narrative writing is telling a story, whether the story is fictional or true. Good narrative writers engage and orient the reader by setting out a clear problem or situation, establishing a point or points of view, and introducing a narrator and/or main characters. In a fictional narrative the problem is almost always a

Name __________ Class __________ Date __________

conflict experienced by the main character(s). Fictional narratives are usually told from the first-person or third-person point of view. A third-person narrator can be anonymous and omniscient, like the narrator of Dickens's *Oliver Twist*, or a participant in the story with a limited understanding of what he or she observes. The first-person narrator of a fictional story is most often the main character.

LEARN FROM THE MODEL

Reread the first five paragraphs of the story (pages 1194–1195) to explore how the author introduces her story's narrator, point-of-view, and conflict.

1. What do you learn about the narrator in these paragraphs? What does the narrator tell you about himself and what can you infer about him from what he says? Write your responses in the graphic organizer that follows.

What The Narrator Says About Himself	What You Can Infer About the Narrator

Narrative

Name ______________________ Class ____________ Date ____________

2. In what ways does the narrator fit the pattern of the first-person point of view in a work of fiction? In what ways does he fit the pattern of the third-person limited point of view? Write your responses in the graphic organizers that follow.

How the Narrator Fits the Pattern of the First-Person Point of View

How the Narrator Fits the Pattern of the Third-Person Point of View

3. How would you describe the problem or conflict the main character encounters in these paragraphs? What additional conflict do we learn about on page 1196? Are these conflicts external or internal?

____

____

____

____

W.11–12.3, a
W.11–12.5

APPLY WHAT YOU'VE LEARNED

4. How will you engage and orient the readers of your story? How will you introduce your narrator, main character(s), and setting? How will you establish a narrative point of view? How will you set out the story's main conflict(s)? Write your responses in the graphic organizer that follows.

Name________________ Class________ Date________

Narrator and Point of View:	Main Character(s):
Setting (Time and Place):	**Conflict(s) and Complication(s):**

Create a Coherent Sequence of Events and Conclusion

Your story should present a smooth progression of experiences or events. Good narrative writers use a variety of techniques to sequence events so that they build on one another to create a coherent whole. They also provide a conclusion that follows from and reflects on what is experienced, observed, or resolved over the course of the narrative.

LEARN FROM THE MODEL

Review the sequence of events in "At the Pitt-Rivers" to explore how the author has created a smooth progression and a coherent whole with a satisfying conclusion.

5. How does the author provide a smooth, logical progression for the sequence of events in "At the Pitt-Rivers"?

____

____

____

____

Narrative

Name_________________________ Class_____________ Date_____________

6. How do the two plot lines in this story—that of the boy and that of the unnamed couple—build on one another to create a coherent whole?

____

____

____

____

7. How does the conclusion of this story follow from and reflect on the resolution of the main character's conflict?

____

____

____

____

Name________________________ Class______________ Date______________

W.11–12.3, a, c
W.11–12.5

APPLY WHAT YOU'VE LEARNED

4. What will be the sequence of events in your narrative? Use as many boxes as you need.

Event:

↓

Event:

↓

Event:

↓

Event:

↓

Event:

↓

Event:

Narrative

Name______________________ Class__________ Date__________

5. What will connect these events to one another? How will this sequence of events create a coherent whole?

____

____

____

6. How will your conclusion show how the events of the story have changed the main character(s) or taught the main character(s) something?

____

____

____

Use Narrative Techniques: Language and Description

W.11–12.3b, 3d

Description is a detailed portrayal of a person, place, or thing. Good writers use elements of description to convey a vivid picture of the setting, experiences, events, and characters or individuals in a narrative.

LEARN FROM THE MODEL

Elements of description include

- precise words and phrases
- sensory language that appeals to the five senses—touch, smell, sound, sight, and taste
- telling details—specific pieces of information that tell the reader something important

1. How do the descriptive words, phrases, details, and sensory language in this story convey vividly the experiences, conflicts, and development of the main character? Write your responses in the graphic organizer that follows.

Language Used	What It Conveys
Precise words and phrases:	
Telling details:	
Sensory language:	

Narrative

Name ______________________ Class ____________ Date ____________

W.11–12.3, b, d
W.11–12.5

APPLY WHAT YOU'VE LEARNED

2. Write sentences in which you describe and elaborate on how you and others look, think, act, feel, and interact at each point in your narrative. Be sure to include

- precise words and phrases
- sensory language that appeals to the five senses
- telling details—specific information that tells the reader something important

Event/Situation:

____

____

____

Interactions and Reactions of Characters:

____

____

____

Event/Situation:

____

____

____

Interactions and Reactions of Characters:

____

____

____

Narrative

Name______________________________ Class______________ Date______________

Event/Situation:

____

____

____

Interactions and Reactions of Characters:

____

____

____

Use Narrative Techniques: Plot Lines

The plot line of a short story usually follows the following progression:

Exposition → Rising Action (Conflict, Complication) → Climax → Falling Action → Resolution

Stories can have a **single plot line** or **multiple plot lines.** In "At the Pitt-Rivers" Penelope Lively develops two separate plot lines, but she weaves them into a single, coherent story with a logical conclusion that resolves both.

LEARN FROM THE MODEL

Review the sequence of events in the story to see how the two plot lines interact and build on one another to create a coherent whole with a satisfying conclusion.

Name________________ Class__________ Date__________

1. Trace the developments in the two subplots and explain how they interact. Write your responses in the graphic organizer below.

The Story of the Boy	How the Stories Interact	The Story of the Couple

Name______________________ Class__________ Date__________

W.11–12.3, b, c, e
W.11–12.5

APPLY WHAT YOU'VE LEARNED

2. Will your story have multiple plot lines or a single plot line? Give reasons for your choice. Then outline your plot(s) in the graphic organizer that follows.

____

____

____

Plot Line(s)		
Exposition		
Rising Action		
Climax		
Falling Action		
Resolution		

Narrative

Name________________________ Class____________ Date____________

Draft

Before you begin drafting, review your prewriting notes on pages 200–209. Then write your first draft on a computer, following the instructions below.

Write the Opening

Begin by writing the opening to your story. In the opening, you should introduce the main character(s) and the conflict. You should also establish the point of view and the character and voice of your narrator.

Add descriptive details about the characters and events in your story from your prewriting notes.

Include Dialogue

As you write, include dialogue to help flesh out the characters and action, enhance the pacing, and move the plot along. Identify the purpose of the dialogue and the type of language you will use to convey each character's personality and purpose in the story. You may also want to communicate some characters' thoughts and feelings.

W.11–12.3, b Use tag lines (phrases such as "said Charlie") to identify each speaker. Avoid using "said" repeatedly in tag lines, and instead use a variety of descriptive words, such as *answered, asked, replied, screamed, shouted, murmured, whispered.*

Write the Body

W.11–12.3, b, c, d Next, use your prewriting notes to write the body of your story. Remember to

- use descriptive details to develop characters and events
- pace the sequence of events you have mapped out so that events build on one another to create a coherent whole
- use narrative techniques, such as dialogue, to develop action and/or characters
- use precise words and phrases, telling details, and sensory language to convey a vivid picture of the characters, setting, and action.

Write the Ending

W.11–12.3, e Finally, write the ending of your story. Make sure that your ending follows from and reflects on what your characters experience, observe, or resolve over the course of the story.

Revise

To revise your story, you will be focusing on the content, or the message, of your writing and possibly applying one or more of these four revision strategies:

Name ______ Class ______ Date ______

- **add** details and information to make the message clearer
- **remove** distracting or unnecessary words or ideas
- **substitute** more precise or stronger words for bland or overused language
- **rearrange** phrases and sentences to be sure the message is logically presented

W.11–12.4

The questions that follow will show you how to use these revision strategies and help you consider how well the development, organization, and style of your story are appropriate to task, purpose, and audience. Evaluate your narrative and check each box when your narrative meets the criteria.

Focus and Coherence

☐ Does my story have a clear focus?

☐ Do all the parts work together so that I achieve my purpose?

☐ Will readers be able to follow the sequence of events?

W11–12.3a, c, e

Organization

☐ Does the beginning introduce the people, conflict, and point of view?

☐ Does the middle use a variety of techniques to sequence events so that they build to create a coherent whole?

☐ Does the ending follow from and reflect on what is experienced, observed, or resolved over the course of the story?

W.11–12.3, b

Development of Ideas

☐ Are the people fully developed?

☐ Are they presented in an interesting, believable, and meaningful way?

☐ Do I use story techniques, such as dialogue, pacing, description, reflection, and multiple plot lines, to develop experiences, events, and/or people?

W.11–12.3d

Voice—Word Choice

☐ Does my writing include precise words and phrases and telling details to convey a vivid picture of the experiences, events, setting, and/or people?

☐ Does my story include sensory language?

Narrative

Voice—Sentence Fluency

☐ Do the sentences vary in length and structure?

☐ Does my writing flow smoothly?

☐ Have I emphasized important points?

Edit and Proofread

Correct Errors in Grammar

Editing involves correcting errors in grammar, usage, mechanics, and spelling.

Begin the editing stage by taking a careful look at your sentences. Make sure that each sentence expresses a complete thought in a way that is grammatically correct. Use the checklist below to edit your sentences.

SENTENCE-EDITING CHECKLIST

☐ Have I avoided sentence fragments?

☐ Have I avoided run-on sentences?

☐ Do verbs agree with their subjects?

☐ Are pronouns used correctly?

☐ Are verbs used correctly?

☐ Have I avoided misplaced and dangling modifiers?

☐ Have I used phrases and clauses correctly?

☐ Have I used parallel structure?

Correct Errors in Mechanics and Spelling

L.11–12.2, b

Next, check for and correct any errors in mechanics (punctuation and capitalization) and spelling.

Use the checklist below to edit your story.

You should also use a dictionary to check and confirm spellings.

PROOFREADING CHECKLIST

☐ Are commas and other punctuation marks used as needed?

☐ Are all words spelled correctly?

☐ Are capital letters used as needed?

Narrative

Name______________________ Class__________ Date__________

Present/Publish

W.11–12.6

After you have written and polished your story, you will want to publish and present it. You may wish to consider some of these publishing and presenting options:

- create a class anthology
- publish your story in an online forum or magazine
- enter your story into a writing contest
- perform your story as readers' theater

Consider using technology, including the Internet, to publish your story, taking advantage of technology's capacity to display information flexibly and dynamically.

Grammar Practice

Hyphenation

A **hyphen (-)** is a punctuation mark that is sometimes required between parts of a compound word or expression and often used in a series of modifiers to avoid confusion. Hyphens are also used at the end of the appropriate syllable when words are broken at the end of a line of text.

L.11–12.2, a, b

Hyphens in Compound Words and Expressions

Some common compound words and expressions *always* require hyphens as part of their correct spelling.

Make sure the three-year-old holds the glass right-side up.

She was twenty-six when she started working. Now she is retired and well-to-do.

Compounds are also often written as a single word or as separate words.

It is a harebrained to flip upside down unless you are doing a full gainer.

There are some rules for deciding which pattern to follow. For example written-out fractions and numbers between twenty-one and ninety-nine are always hyphenated.

Is the total two-thirds or one-and-two-thirds?

We won seventeen thousand, four hundred and ninety-eight dollars.

Another general rule is that compounds that are written as separate words to form nouns are often hyphenated to form adjectives or adverbs. Predicate adjectives are an exception to this rule.

The soldier appeared at the ball in full dress [noun].

It was a full-dress [adjective] occasion.

The occasion was definitely full dress [predicate adjective].

Name______________________________ Class______________ Date______________

However, the three ways of spelling compound words—separated, joined, and hyphenated—do not always follow clear and consistent rules, so the best method for knowing how to write them correctly is to look them up in a dictionary.

Exercise A: Using Hyphens with Compound Words and Expressions

Identify the compound word or expression containing the words that precede each sentence. Then insert the correct form of the compound word or expression into the sentence where indicated. Use a dictionary or other spelling resource to check your work.

man; hour

1. How many ______________ did the factory lose during the storm?

deep; space

2. Voyager has been in ______________ for many years now.

test; tube

3. This ______________ contains a miracle drug.

bitter; sweet

4. The goodbye ceremony was a ______________ occasion.

dead; man's; float

5. The only kind of swimming I can do is the ______________.

Hyphens in Series of Modifiers

L.11-12.2, a, b

Hyphens are sometimes used to clarify relationships between modifiers in a series. In this case the use of the hyphen is not required by the words themselves but by how they are used. For example, the following sentence is ambiguous.

The exotic flower arrangement pleased everyone.

The sentence could refer to an arrangement of exotic flowers (1). Or it could refer to an exotic arrangement of flowers (2). The adjective *exotic* can modify either *flower* or *arrangement*. The ambiguity can be eliminated through the use of hyphens.

(1) The exotic-flower arrangement pleased everyone.

(2) The exotic flower-arrangement pleased everyone.

Avoid inserting hyphens into a series of modifiers when there is no logical ambiguity.

Narrative

The amazingly exotic flowers pleased everyone.

This sentence can refer only to flowers that are amazingly exotic. The adverb *amazingly* can modify only *exotic*. No hyphen is needed.

Exercise B: Using Hyphens in a Series of Modifiers

Write the following sentences correctly, inserting hyphens into the underlined portions when they are needed.

6. The big rig driver ordered breakfast. (The rig driver is small and thin.)

____

7. Are you in favor of the continued deep space exploration?

____

8. The sergeant gave out three day passes, so each of the recipients got a day off.

____

9. Have you ever studied the art of Japanese flower arranging? (You can use flowers from all over the world.)

____

10. That was a richly satisfying novel that I read.

____

L.11-12.2, a, b

Hyphens with Prefixes

In general, a hyphen should not be used after a prefix unless what follows is a proper noun. Some other exceptions are the prefixes *all-*, *ex-* (meaning "former"), *self-*, and *cross-* when joined to any noun or adjective, and *anti-* with a word that begins with *i*. Use a hyphen after *vice-*, except in *vice president*.

Some places in sub-Saharan Africa are heavily hit by malaria and have substandard medical resources.

She is a self-identified social activist.

The use of DDT as an antimosquito pesticide is not as anti-ideological as it sounds.

Name________________________________ Class________________ Date________________

Be careful not to confuse two different words containing the same letters. For example, a city that used to be a port is an ex-port, but a product that is sold abroad is an export.

Exercise C: Using Hyphens with Prefixes

On the line before each item, write **C** or **I** to identify the hyphen as correctly or incorrectly used with a prefix.

___**11.** anti-DDT

___**12.** re-introduce

___**13.** all-inclusive

___**14.** exopponent

___**15.** self-examination

Hyphens for End-of-Line Word Breaks

L.11–12.2, a, b

A word must sometimes be divided at the end of a line for space considerations. The dictionary is the best guide to where syllables are best divided, but some general principles may be helpful.

It is not acceptable to break a word after or before a single letter, nor is it acceptable to break a single-syllable word. *Event, choosy, should,* and *through,* for example, cannot be divided. Breaking words that may be misread if divided incorrectly or dividing so that only the last two letters of a word go to a new line should be avoided.

Check Your Writing

Read through your narrative to check for and correct any errors you may have made in the use of hyphens. Use a dictionary or other spelling reference-work as needed.

Narrative

Vocabulary

Name ______________________ Class ____________ Date ____________

L.11–12.4
L.11–12.4a
L.11–12.4b
L.11–12.4c
L.11–12.4d

Context as Clues to Meaning

In this lesson you will explore how the context in which an unfamiliar word appears may provide clues to its meaning. A word's context includes the other words around it in the same sentence, other sentences, and even paragraphs nearby. Context often contains information that you can use to infer the meaning of an unfamiliar word

The context of a word may tell you only its part of speech. The only information provided about *imminent* in the sentence "Their arrival was imminent" is that it is an adjective. It could mean "late," "worth waiting for," "unlikely" or any number of other things. The fact that it means "soon to occur; ready to take place" is not hinted at in any way.

The other extreme case is when a word's context provides its exact meaning. For example, "Of course, they had their foibles, those minor flaws in character or behavior, which, one must admit, most people have."

Even when there are useful context clues for the meaning of an unfamiliar word, they usually provide only a general sense of what the word means. This may be enough to meet your needs. When it is not, you must use a dictionary or glossary to check for the precise meaning. Since many words have more than one meaning, you may have to look through a number of definitions for the word before you find one that matches its use in a particular sentence.

L.11–12.4
L.11–12.4a
L.11–12.4d
L.11–12.5
L.11–12.6

Context Clues Based on Word Relationships

Two of the most common kinds of context clues are synonyms and antonyms. For example, "Fear of sudden, loud noises is innate. Because it is inborn, we do not learn it." These sentences clearly suggest that *innate* is a synonym for *inborn*. In a similar fashion, "Some people find a certain scent to be delightfully fragrant, while others think it malodorous" suggests that *malodorous* means "foul smelling" by providing a contrast to *fragrant*.

You should always test your inference about an unfamiliar word's meaning in the context of the sentence. For example, "Some people find a certain scent to be delightfully fragrant, while others think it is foul smelling" makes sense. When an inference doesn't make sense, that is a clear signal that it is wrong.

Name ______________________ Class ______________ Date ____________

Exercise A: Use Context Clues Based on Word Relationships

Use context clues to infer the meaning of the underlined word. Circle the letter corresponding to the best equivalent to the word's meaning. Remember to check your inference.

1. Ted was irate, and I had never seen him so furious.

a. loud
b. angry
c. lazy
d. surprised

2. To receive criticism for her actions when she had expected kudos was both disappointing and confusing to her.

a. blame
b. ignorance
c. praise
d. immediate action

3. His first efforts were lethargic, but as he saw how successful he was, he became significantly livelier.

a. sluggish
b. energetic
c. exhausting
d. determined

4. She comments on every little mistake I make, no matter how miniscule it may be.

a. obvious
b. ridiculous
c. important
d. tiny

5. Vince has become a new person, abandoning his once ignoble behavior and replacing it with praiseworthy actions.

a. old
b. careful
c. shameful
d. impressive

Vocabulary

Name ______________________________ Class ______________ Date ______________

L.11–12.4
L.11–12.4a
L.11–12.4d
L.11–12.6

Context Clues Based on Description or Contrast

A similar kind of context clue provides description or contrast rather than a specific synonym or antonym. For example, "She didn't have to think at all about the task; the work required only mindless effort." There is no synonym for *mindless*, but it is clear that it means something similar to "requiring little attention or thought." In a similar fashion, contrast may be provided. "Over time, her muscles became less stiff and rigid, and her suppleness increased." Although there is no antonym for *suppleness*, the contrast provided by "less stiff and rigid" suggests that it means *something* similar to "flexibility."

Exercise B: Use Context Clues Based on Description or Contrast

Use context clues to infer the meaning of the underlined word. Circle the letter corresponding to the best equivalent to the word's meaning. Remember to check your inference.

6. The news made her grin broadly and skip with happiness, which was a distinct change from her formerly morose mood.

a. tired
b. aimless
c. unhappy
d. determined

7. He tried to show how penitent he was with a sincere and heartfelt apology.

a. sorry
b. different
c. angry
d. lucky

8. Instead of just quickly getting to the point, the speaker gave a protracted speech.

a. long
b. brief
c. foolish
d. thoughtful

9. I was offered 50 cents to do the work and considered that a pittance, given that it would have taken me at least an hour to do it.

a. mistake
b. good deal
c. fair wage
d. small amount

10. The <u>proximity</u> of the lamp made it easy for me to reach out and turn it on without getting up.

a. tallness
b. usefulness
c. nearness
d. brightness

L.11–12.4
L.11–12.4a
L.11–12.4d
L.11–12.6

Context Clues Based on Examples

Some context clues provide examples that allow you to figure out what an unfamiliar word means. For example, "Mice, possums, and raccoons are all <u>nocturnal</u> animals, but the one best known for this characteristic is the owl." The examples given by the sentence, especially given that the owl is named as a particularly well-known one, suggest that *nocturnal* means something like "awake or active at night."

Exercise C: Use Context Clues Based on Examples

Use context clues to infer the meaning of the underlined word. Circle the letter corresponding to the best equivalent to the word's meaning. Remember to check your inference.

11. My little brother's <u>plaintive</u> noises included heavy sighs, moans, and soft whining.

a. loud
b. infuriated
c. selfish
d. melancholy

12. She <u>gesticulated</u> as she spoke by pounding one fist into the other palm, waving her arms, and occasionally giving the "thumbs-up" sign.

a. hesitated
b. made noise
c. made gestures
d. showed bad taste

13. His <u>exhortations</u> to leave included "Hurry up!" "Let's go!" and "Get a move on!"

a. jokes
b. refusals
c. suggestions
d. strong urgings

Name ______________________ Class __________ Date __________

14. They responded with jeers, mockery, and other indications that they thought my behavior was ludicrous.

a. absurd
b. amusing
c. frightening
d. respectable

15. She demonstrated her egotism by talking about herself constantly, bragging, and strutting everywhere she went.

a. sensitivity
b. friendliness
c. conceit
d. greed

L.11–12.4
L.11–12.4a
L.11–12.4d
L.11–12.6

Context Clues Based on General Reasoning

Even when context clues do not fall into a particular category, you can sometimes figure out the meaning of an unfamiliar word by applying logical reasoning. For example, look at this sentence: "The factory smokestack emitted dark clouds." Your own experience of seeing smokestacks allows you to figure out that *emitted* must mean "gave off" or "released." Context clues help you use what you do know to figure out what you don't know.

Exercise D: Use Context Clues Based On General Reasoning

Use context clues to infer the meaning of the underlined word. Circle the letter corresponding to the best equivalent to the word's meaning. Remember to check your inference.

16. I was discouraged by the length of the queue outside the movie theater and wondered if there would still be tickets available when I got to the front of it.

a. line
b. expense
c. poster
d. parking lot

17. People called "town criers" used to disseminate the news, but now we have TV news stations, daily newspapers, and electronic media to handle this job.

a. create
b. subdue
c. spread
d. change

Name ______________________ Class ____________ Date ____________

18. So insulting your boss got you fired, did it? Well, what did you think the ramifications of such behavior might be?

a. causes
b. actions
c. compliments
d. consequences

19. His teacher extolled his paper in front of the class as being exceptionally good, so Sam was pretty sure he'd received an A on it.

a. graded
b. praised
c. criticized
d. disposed of

20. I gasped at the stench of the rotten food and had to hold my nose.

a. sight
b. stink
c. cost
d. wastefulness

Name ____________________ Class ____________ Date ____________

L.11–12.4, b, c, d
L.11–12.5, a
L.11–12.6

Patterns of Word Changes

In this lesson you will explore how to use what you know about patterns of word changes to figure out word meanings. First, you will look at suffixes and how they affect meaning. Then you will learn how to use familiar words to infer the meanings of unfamiliar words with the same root or base.

L.11–12.4
L.11–12.4b
L.11–12.4c
L.11–12.6

How Suffixes Affect Meaning

A suffix is a word part added to the end of a base word or root (if the base is not a word) to change its meaning. The effect may be slight, as when *–ed* or *–ing* is added to a verb to change its tense. However, many suffixes modify the meaning of a word in more significant ways, often by changing its part of speech.

Some suffixes and the ways they affect meaning will be familiar to you. For example, even though you have probably never seen the word *synonymity* before, the chances are good that you understand what it means to recognize the synonymity of *big* and *large*. That's because you're familiar with using the *–ity* suffix to form a noun, as in *morality* and *responsibility*. Similarly, you're familiar with the adjective-forming suffix *–ative*, as in *talkative* and *informative*.

It can be helpful to use what you know about familiar suffixes to figure out the meanings of unfamiliar words that use those suffixes. Bear in mind that adding suffixes often changes the spelling of a base word, most often by dropping a final *e* or changing it to an *i* or by doubling a final consonant.

Of course, the only way to be sure about a word's precise meaning, no matter how much you know about its parts, is to look in a dictionary or glossary.

Exercise A: Use Familiar Suffixes to Determine Meaning

Think about the meaning of each underlined word's base word or root and suffix to figure out the meaning of the word. Circle the letter of the correct answer.

1. One object known for its solidity is a

a. cloud **b.** brick **c.** raindrop

2. A product that is meant to have curative power is called

a. a car **b.** a book **c.** a medicine

3. The perpendicularity of a cliff wall is one way to measure its

a. length **b.** stability **c.** steepness

4. Having a transformative experience would be sure to

a. change you **b.** scare you **c.** delight you

5. The authenticity of an item is a determination of how

a. real it is **b.** costly it is **c.** useful it is

Vocabulary

Name ______________________ Class ____________ Date ____________

Not all suffixes are as familiar as *–ity* and *–ative*. Here are some common suffixes found in English words that affect the part of speech of the base word or root:

Noun-Forming Suffixes	Examples
–age	breakage, marriage
–tude	multitude, gratitude
Adjective-Forming Suffixes	**Examples**
–ious	fictitious, harmonious
–ory	contradictory, satisfactory

The presence of these letters at the end of a word does not necessarily mean that they function as these types of suffixes. For example, *–age* is not a suffix at all in *birdcage*, and *–ory* does not form an adjective in *history* or *category*. When you come across a word that has a suffix that usually creates a certain part of speech, you should not assume the word is that part of speech. Check how the word functions in the sentence. If a word with a suffix that often forms an adjective is functioning in a sentence as a different part of speech, you should look in a dictionary or glossary to find out the word's meaning.

Exercise B: Use Suffixes to Determine Part of Speech and Meaning

Use the chart above and your knowledge of base words and roots to answer the following questions. Write your answers on the lines.

6. What part of speech is spoilage most likely to be? ____________

7. You might expect to find seepage under ____________

8. What part of speech is habitude most likely to be? ____________

9. Someone who exists in involuntary servitude is called a ____________

10. What part of speech is investigatory most likely to be? ____________

11. One type of celebratory event is a ____________

12. What part of speech is censorious most likely to be? ____________

13. A person whose behavior has been meritorious might receive ____________

Name ______________________ Class __________ Date __________

L.11–12.4b
L.11–12.4c
L.11–12.4d
L.11–12.6

Using What You Know About Familiar Words

Learning vocabulary is easier than it might be because we do not have to learn every word independently of all other words. When you learned the meaning of *define*, you also learned a great deal about *definition, undefined, definitive, definable, misdefine,* and *definite*.

Most words have connections to other words, and you can use those connections to figure out meanings:

> *indomitable* = *in–* plus *domit* plus *–able*
>
> *dom* is a root found in *dominate, dominant,* and *domineer*, all of which have to do with power and control
>
> *in–* is a common negating prefix
>
> *–able* is a suffix that means "able to"
>
> *indomitable* probably means "not able to be controlled"

You will not necessarily know exactly what an unfamiliar word means, even if you know quite a bit about all of its parts, but you can often get a good idea of its meaning. You should always look carefully at an unfamiliar word to see if you recognize any part or parts of it.

> *antipathy* contains *path*
>
> *path* is found in *sympathy* and *pathetic* and seems to have to do with feelings
>
> *anti–* means "against"

You may not be sure of the exact meaning of *antipathy*, which is "strong dislike," but you know something about it. You know it has to do with "a feeling against," so if you read that a man "felt antipathy for snakes," you could be pretty sure that he didn't like snakes.

As always, the best way to get information about the exact meaning of a word is to look it up in a dictionary or glossary.

Name ______________________ Class ____________ Date ____________

Exercise C: Use Familiar Words to Determine Meanings of Unfamiliar Words

For each item, think about what you know about a familiar word or words to infer the meaning of the underlined word. Circle the letter of the correct answer. Check your inferences in context or in a dictionary.

14. By thinking about *disprove* and *possess*, you can tell that to dispossess someone of something is to

a. give it **b.** take it **c.** ignore it

15. By thinking about *gullible*, you can tell that to gull people would be to

a. mystify them **b.** cheer them **c.** deceive them

16. By thinking about *infinite*, you can tell that something finite has

a. limits **b.** beauty **c.** reality

17. By thinking about *lack* and *luster*, you can tell that something lackluster is

a. dull **b.** invisible **c.** delightful

18. By thinking about *nonsense* and *committed*, you can tell that a noncommittal reply to a question would be

a. "Yes" **b.** "No" **c.** "Maybe"

19. By thinking about *bountiful*, you can tell that bounty is

a. a decoration **b.** generosity **c.** politeness

20. By thinking about *irresponsible* and *reproach*, you can tell that an irreproachable person is

a. happy **b.** blameless **c.** ungrateful

L.11–12.4b
L.11–12.4d
L.11–12.5a
L.11–12.6

How Meanings Change

The meanings of words change over time. They may broaden, become more narrow, or change in other ways. For example, *meat* once meant "food," but, over many years, the meaning contracted to what it means now. The original meaning of *gloom* was as a verb, "to look displeased; to frown." The meaning grew to include "to look threatening," and then, finally, changed to have its current meaning as a noun.

Name ______________________ Class ____________ Date ____________

One way in which meanings change is by association. If a word is used by enough people over enough time in a figurative way, that meaning will become part of the dictionary definition of the word. For example, *summit* was once used only to describe the topmost part of a hill, a meaning it still has. But the meaning grew as people used the word figuratively to refer to the summit of a person's career or to a meeting of national leaders as a "summit conference."

We often learn one meaning of a word, such as *dawn*, and then see or hear it used in a way that doesn't make sense, such as "The truth began to dawn on me." How could truth begin to dawn? By gradually becoming visible, as the sun does when it comes up. This figurative meaning of *dawn* is now part of the dictionary definition of the word.

When you come across a word you know, but the familiar meaning doesn't fit the context, try thinking of how the meaning of the word may have grown over time to include a more figurative sense.

Exercise D: Understand Meanings that Come from Other Meanings

For each item, think about a meaning or meanings you know in order to infer the meaning of the underlined word. Circle the letter of the correct answer. Check your inferences in context or in a dictionary.

21. By thinking about the meaning you know for *bridle*, you could guess that unbridled enthusiasm is

a. mild **b.** unjustified **c.** unrestrained

22. By thinking about the meaning you know for *tart*, you could guess that to give a response tartly is to give it

a. slowly **b.** sharply **c.** jokingly

23. By thinking about the meanings you know for *spit* and *fire*, you could guess that a spitfire is someone who is

a. calm **b.** cheerful **c.** hot-tempered

24. By thinking about the meaning you know for *wedge*, you could guess that to wedge something into a space is to

a. force it in **b.** slip it in quickly **c.** delicately insert it

25. By thinking about the meaning you know for *grip*, you could guess that a gripping story is one that

a. bores you **b.** amuses you **c.** holds your attention

Name ______________________ Class ____________ Date ______________

L.11–12.4, c, d
L.11–12.5, b
L.11–12.6

Synonyms: Nuances

Synonyms are words that mean the same or *almost the same* thing. Small differences in meaning among synonyms are called "nuances" or "shades of meaning." Almost all synonyms vary, at least slightly, in their dictionary definitions. In addition, some synonyms have different connotations—differences in associations that enrich their meanings beyond their dictionary definitions. Consider, for example, the differences in meaning between the synonyms *stubborn, persistent, determined, headstrong, obstinate,* and *pigheaded.*

L.11–12.5b

Recognizing Nuances

Synonyms differ from each other in their degree of intensity, in how positive or how negative they are, and in a variety of other ways. For example, *gush* and *squirt* are synonyms, but *gush* is much more extreme. Similarly, *childlike* and *childish* are synonyms, but *childlike* is more positive than *childish.*

Exercise A: Recognize Nuances

Answer the following questions on the lines provided. You may use a dictionary if you are unsure of the answer.

1. How is a fad different from a fashion?

____

____

2. How is a clique different from a group?

____

____

3. How is grip different from hold?

____

____

4. How is tap different from hit?

____

____

5. How is a fib different from a lie?

____

____

Name ______________________ Class __________ Date __________

L.11–12.4c
L.11–12.4d
L.11–12.5b

Analyze Nuances

A thesaurus is undoubtedly valuable, but it is rare for one to explain the differences among the synonyms it lists for a word. Unless you are sure you understand what they are, you should never rely on a thesaurus by itself. A dictionary, on the other hand, will tell you precisely what words mean.

When you are reading, having a good idea of the general meaning of a word is usually sufficient. When you are writing, however, it is not. In order to communicate effectively, you must know exactly what the words you use mean. If you do not, you may well end up communicating something quite different from what you intended. If you're not absolutely sure of the meaning of a word, you must check it in a dictionary.

Exercise B: Analyze Nuances

Read the synonyms for each word given below and then answer the questions about them. Do not use the same answer for more than one question. You may use a dictionary if you are unsure of the answer.

think: muse, ponder, reflect, speculate, imagine

run: scamper, flee, lope, sprint, bolt

6. Which synonym for *think* communicates the idea of thinking about something that already occurred? ______________

7. Which synonym for *think* communicates the idea of thinking in a way based on invention or fancy? ______________

8. Which synonym for *think* communicates the idea of thinking in a particularly slow and careful way? ______________

9. Which synonym for *think* communicates the idea of thinking that is based on little or no evidence? ______________

10. Which synonym for *think* communicates the idea of thinking in a leisurely, dreamlike way? ______________

11. Which synonym for *run* communicates the idea of running from danger? ______________

12. Which synonym for *run* communicates the idea of running that starts out very suddenly? ______________

Name ______________________ Class __________ Date __________

13. Which synonym for *run* communicates the idea of running in a leisurely, loose-limbed way? ______________

14. Which synonym for *run* communicates the idea of running at top speed for a short distance? ______________

15. Which synonym for *run* communicates the idea of running playfully? ______________

Grades 11–12 Common Core State Standards

Grades 11–12 Common Core State Standards

Reading Standards for Literature

Key Ideas and Details

1. Cite strong and thorough textual evidence to support analysis of what the text says explicitly as well as inferences drawn from the text, including determining where the text leaves matters uncertain.
2. Determine two or more themes or central ideas of a text and analyze their development over the course of the text, including how they interact and build on one another to produce a complex account; provide an objective summary of the text.
3. Analyze the impact of the author's choices regarding how to develop and relate elements of a story or drama (e.g., where a story is set, how the action is ordered, how the characters are introduced and developed).

Craft and Structure

4. Determine the meaning of words and phrases as they are used in the text, including figurative and connotative meanings; analyze the impact of specific word choices on meaning and tone, including words with multiple meanings or language that is particularly fresh, engaging, or beautiful. (Include Shakespeare as well as other authors.)
5. Analyze how an author's choices concerning how to structure specific parts of a text (e.g., the choice of where to begin or end a story, the choice to provide a comedic or tragic resolution) contribute to its overall structure and meaning as well as its aesthetic impact.
6. Analyze a case in which grasping point of view requires distinguishing what is directly stated in a text from what is really meant (e.g., satire, sarcasm, irony, or understatement).

Integration of Knowledge and Ideas

7. Analyze multiple interpretations of a story, drama, or poem (e.g., recorded or live production of a play or recorded novel or poetry), evaluating how each version interprets the source text. (Include at least one play by Shakespeare and one play by an American dramatist.).
8. (Not applicable to literature)
9. Demonstrate knowledge of eighteenth–, nineteenth– and early–twentieth–century foundational works of American literature, including how two or more texts from the same period treat similar themes or topics.

Range of Reading and Level of Text Complexity

10. By the end of grade 12, read and comprehend literature, including stories, dramas, and poems, at the high end of the grades 11–CCR text complexity band independently and proficiently.

Reading Standards for Informational Text

Key Ideas and Details

1. Cite strong and thorough textual evidence to support analysis of what the text says explicitly as well as inferences drawn from the text, including determining where the text leaves matters uncertain.
2. Determine two or more central ideas of a text and analyze their development over the course of the text, including how they interact and build on one another to provide a complex analysis; provide an objective summary of the text.
3. Analyze a complex set of ideas or sequence of events and explain how specific individuals, ideas, or events interact and develop over the course of the text.

Craft and Structure

4. Determine the meaning of words and phrases as they are used in a text, including figurative, connotative, and technical meanings; analyze how an author uses and refines the meaning of a key term or terms over the course of a text (e.g., how Madison defines *faction* in *Federalist* No. 10)..
5. Analyze and evaluate the effectiveness of the structure an author uses in his or her exposition or argument, including whether the structure makes points clear, convincing, and engaging.
6. Determine an author's point of view or purpose in a text in which the rhetoric is particularly effective, analyzing how style and content contribute to the power, persuasiveness, or beauty of the text.

Integration of Knowledge and Ideas

7. Integrate and evaluate multiple sources of information presented in different media or formats (e.g., visually, quantitatively) as well as in words in order to address a question or solve a problem.
8. Delineate and evaluate the reasoning in seminal U.S. texts, including the application of constitutional principles and use of legal reasoning (e.g., in U.S. Supreme Court majority opinions and dissents) and the premises, purposes, and arguments in works of public advocacy (e.g., *The Federalist*, presidential addresses).
9. Analyze seventeenth–, eighteenth–, and nineteenth–century foundational U.S. documents of historical and literary significance (including The Declaration of Independence, the Preamble to the Constitution, the Bill of Rights, and Lincoln's Second Inaugural Address) for their themes, purposes, and rhetorical features.

Range of Reading and Level of Text Complexity

10. By the end of grade 12, read and comprehend literary nonfiction at the high end of the grades 11–CCR text complexity band independently and proficiently.

Writing Standards

Text Types and Purposes

1. Write arguments to support claims in an analysis of substantive topics or texts, using valid reasoning and relevant and sufficient evidence.

a. Introduce precise, knowledgeable claim(s), establish the significance of the claim(s), distinguish the claim(s) from alternate or opposing claims, and create an organization that logically sequences claim(s), counterclaims, reasons, and evidence.

b. Develop claim(s) and counterclaims fairly and thoroughly, supplying the most relevant evidence for each while pointing out the strengths and limitations of both in a manner that anticipates the audience's knowledge level, concerns, values, and possible biases.

c. Use words, phrases, and clauses as well as varied syntax to link the major sections of the text, create cohesion, and clarify the relationships between claim(s) and reasons, between reasons and evidence, and between claim(s) and counterclaims.

d. Establish and maintain a formal style and objective tone while attending to the norms and conventions of the discipline in which they are writing.

e. Provide a concluding statement or section that follows from and supports the argument presented.

2. Write informative/explanatory texts to examine and convey complex ideas, concepts, and information clearly and accurately through the effective selection, organization, and analysis of content.

a. Introduce a topic; organize complex ideas, concepts, and information so that each new element builds on that which precedes it to create a unified whole; include formatting (e.g., headings), graphics (e.g., figures, tables), and multimedia when useful to aiding comprehension.

b. Develop the topic thoroughly by selecting the most significant and relevant facts, extended definitions, concrete details, quotations, or other information and examples appropriate to the audience's knowledge of the topic.

c. Use appropriate and varied transitions and syntax to link the major sections of the text, create cohesion, and clarify the relationships among complex ideas and concepts.

d. Use precise language, domain–specific vocabulary, and techniques such as metaphor, simile, and analogy to manage the complexity of the topic.

e. Establish and maintain a formal style and objective tone while attending to the norms and conventions of the discipline in which they are writing.

f. Provide a concluding statement or section that follows from and supports the information or explanation presented (e.g., articulating implications or the significance of the topic).

3. Write narratives to develop real or imagined experiences or events using effective technique, well–chosen details, and well–structured event sequences.

   a. Engage and orient the reader by setting out a problem, situation, or observation and its significance, establishing one or multiple point(s) of view, and introducing a narrator and/or characters; create a smooth progression of experiences or events.

   b. Use narrative techniques, such as dialogue, pacing, description, reflection, and multiple plot lines, to develop experiences, events, and/or characters.

   c. Use a variety of techniques to sequence events so that they build on one another to create a coherent whole and build toward a particular tone and outcome (e.g., a sense of mystery, suspense, growth, or resolution).

   d. Use precise words and phrases, telling details, and sensory language to convey a vivid picture of the experiences, events, setting, and/or characters.

   e. Provide a conclusion that follows from and reflects on what is experienced, observed, or resolved over the course of the narrative.

Production and Distribution of Writing

4. Produce clear and coherent writing in which the development, organization, and style are appropriate to task, purpose, and audience. (Grade-specific expectations for writing types are defined in standards 1–3 above.)

5. Develop and strengthen writing as needed by planning, revising, editing, rewriting, or trying a new approach, focusing on addressing what is most significant for a specific purpose and audience. (Editing for conventions should demonstrate command of Language standards 1–3 up to and including grades 11–12.)

6. Use technology, including the Internet, to produce, publish, and update individual or shared writing products in response to ongoing feedback, including new arguments or information.

Research to Build and Present Knowledge

7. Conduct short as well as more sustained research projects to answer a question (including a self-generated question) or solve a problem; narrow or broaden the inquiry when appropriate; synthesize multiple sources on the subject, demonstrating understanding of the subject under investigation.

8. Gather relevant information from multiple authoritative print and digital sources, using advanced searches effectively; assess the strengths and limitations of each source in terms of the task, purpose, and audience; integrate information into the text selectively to maintain the flow of ideas, avoiding plagiarism and overreliance on any one source and following a standard format for citation.

9. Draw evidence from literary or informational texts to support analysis, reflection, and research.
   a. Apply *grades 11–12 Reading standards* to literature (e.g., "Demonstrate knowledge of eighteenth-, nineteenth-, and early twentieth-century foundational works of American literature, including how two or more texts from the same period treat similar themes or topics").
   b. Apply *grades 11–12 Reading standards* to literary nonfiction (e.g., "Delineate and evaluate the reasoning in seminal U.S. texts, including the application of constitutional principles and use of legal reasoning [e.g., in U.S. Supreme Court Case majority opinions and dissents] and the premises, purposes, and arguments in works of public advocacy [e.g., The Federalist, presidential addresses]").

Range of Writing

10. Write routinely over extended time frames (time for research, reflection, and revision) and shorter time frames (a single sitting or a day or two) for a range of tasks, purposes, and audiences.

Speaking and Listening Standards

Comprehension and Collaboration

1. Initiate and participate effectively in a range of collaborative discussions (one-on-one, in groups, and teacher-led) with diverse partners on *grades 11–12 topics, texts, and issues,* building on others' ideas and expressing their own clearly and persuasively.
   a. Come to discussions prepared, having read and researched material under study; explicitly draw on that preparation by referring to evidence from texts and other research on the topic or issue to stimulate a thoughtful, well-reasoned exchange of ideas.
   b. Work with peers to promote civil, democratic discussions and decision-making, set clear goals and deadlines, and establish individual roles as needed.
   c. Propel conversations by posing and responding to questions that probe reasoning and evidence; ensure a hearing for a full range of positions on a topic or issue; clarify, verify, or challenge ideas and conclusions; and promote divergent and creative perspectives.
   d. Respond thoughtfully to diverse perspectives, summarize comments, claims, and evidence made on all sides of an issue; resolve contradictions when possible; and determine what additional information or research is required to deepen the investigation or complete the task.

2. Integrate multiple sources of information presented in diverse formats and media (e.g., visually, quantitatively, orally) in order to make informed decisions and solve problems, evaluating the credibility and accuracy of each source and noting any discrepancies among the data.
3. Evaluate a speaker's point of view, reasoning, and use of evidence and rhetoric, assessing the stance of premises, links among ideas, word choice, points of emphasis, and tone used.

Presentation of Knowledge and Ideas

4. Present information, findings, and supporting evidence, conveying a clear and distinct perspective, such that listeners can follow the line of reasoning, alternative or opposing perspectives are addressed, and the organization, development, substance, and style are appropriate to purpose, audience, and a range of formal and informal tasks.
5. Make strategic use of digital media (e.g., textual, graphical, audio, visual, and interactive elements) in presentations to enhance understanding of findings, reasoning, and evidence and to add interest.
6. Adapt speech to a variety of contexts and tasks, demonstrating command of formal English when indicated or appropriate. (See grades 11–12 Language standards 1 and 3 for specific expectations.)

Language Standards

Conventions of Standard English

1. Demonstrate command of the conventions of standard English grammar and usage when writing or speaking.
   a. Apply the understanding that usage is a matter of convention, can change over time, and is sometimes contested.
   b. Resolve issues of complex or contested usage, consulting references (e.g., *Merriam-Webster's Dictionary of English Usage, Garner's Modern American Usage*) as needed.
2. Demonstrate command of the conventions of standard English capitalization, punctuation, and spelling when writing.
   a. Observe hyphenation conventions.
   b. Spell correctly.

Knowledge of Language

3. Apply knowledge of language to understand how language functions in different contexts, to make effective choices for meaning or style, and to comprehend more fully when reading or listening.
   a. Vary syntax for effect, consulting references (e.g., Tufte's *Artful Sentences*) for guidance as needed; apply an understanding of syntax to the study of complex texts when reading.

Vocabulary Acquisition and Use

4. Determine or clarify the meaning of unknown and multiple-meaning words and phrases based on *grades 11–12 reading and content*, choosing flexibly from a range of strategies.
   - a. Use context (e.g., the overall meaning of a sentence, paragraph, or text; a word's position or function in a sentence) as a clue to the meaning of a word or phrase.
   - b. Identify and correctly use patterns of word changes that indicate different meanings or parts of speech (e.g., *conceive, conception, conceivable*).
   - c. Consult general and specialized reference materials (e.g., dictionaries, glossaries, thesauruses), both print and digital, to find the pronunciation of a word or determine or clarify its precise meaning, its part of speech, its etymology, or its standard usage.
   - d. Verify the preliminary determination of the meaning of a word or phrase (e.g., by checking the inferred meaning in context or in a dictionary).
5. Demonstrate understanding of figurative language, word relationships, and nuances in word meanings.
   - a. Interpret figures of speech (e.g., hyperbole, paradox) in context and analyze their role in the text.
   - b. Analyze nuances in the meaning of words with similar denotations.
6. Acquire and use accurately general academic and domain-specific words and phrases, sufficient for reading, writing, speaking, and listening at the college and career readiness level; demonstrate independence in gathering vocabulary knowledge when considering a word or phrase important to comprehension or expression.